Mrs. Kamali Would Like to Speak to You About Cloud

Mrs. Kamali Would Like

Melody Martin

to Speak to You About Cloud

Notes from a California Classroom

The Dial Press New York

Published by
The Dial Press
1 Dag Hammarskjold Plaza
New York, New York 10017

Manufactured in the United States of America
First printing

Design by Ann Gold

Library of Congress Cataloging in Publication Data

Martin, Melody.
Mrs. Kamali would like to speak to you about Cloud.

1. Martin, Melody. 2. Teachers—California—Biography. 3. High school students—California. I. Title.
LA2317.M276A35 371.1'0092'4 [B] 80-11408
ISBN 0-8037-6003-5

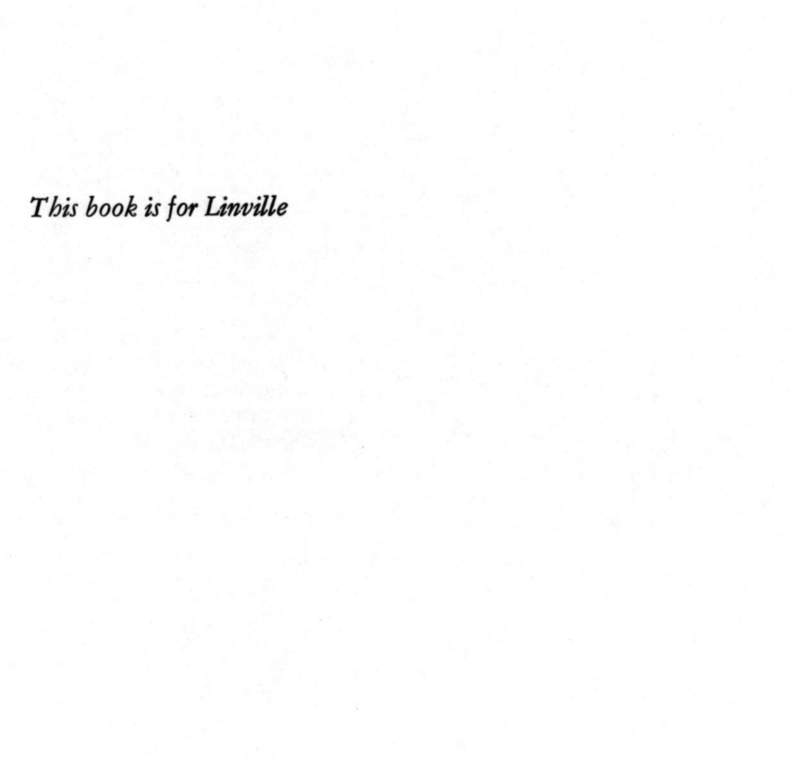

This book is for Linville

Acknowledgments

I would like to thank the following people, who played such important roles in the publication of my first book:

Sandra Elkin, a special and unique literary agent.

Joyce Johnson, a fair and excellent editor.

Dottie Cabe, a constant fan and a fast typist.

And of course my family, my students, and my friends.

Contents

Introduction: To Whom It May Concern *1*

A Local Habitation and a Name *6*

Juicy Brucie, or Take Me to the Drive-in *15*

Princess Grace *25*

The Paraquat Papers *37*

Portrait of the Artist as a Young Woman *51*

Karmic Pole-vaulting in the Ionosphere *64*

Read 'em and Weep *76*

Song of Sappho *89*

Woe Is Me at Wounded Knee *101*

The Vatican Connection *114*

Mother and Child *126*

Dark Shadows *139*

High Tea and Crumpets *149*

Huarached Socrates *163*

Showdown at the Karamazov Corral *177*

Notes from the Underground *190*

Sweet Somethings *208*

Mrs. Kamali Would Like to Speak to You About Cloud

Introduction: To Whom It May Concern

TO WHOM IT MAY CONCERN:

I killed myself because the only thing I was good at was racing motorcycles and that I'm not doing as good in math as I thought and I don't think I could stand getting yelled at again. It was nice having you as parents. Sometime now dad can have a bike, mine. I hope I can kill myself right 12:20.

P.S. I'm sorry for wrecking your carpet

12:30 2–22–78

With my luck I'll live and be a lemon.

Your son
Peter

It was the quietest faculty meeting I've ever attended. Mr. Tozer called an emergency session by posting a huge announcement over our mailboxes. The word *mandatory* consistently produces annoyance, regardless of the agenda.

We were half-awake, foul-humored, and irritated that valuable preparation time had been snatched away for what was probably some painfully trivial nonsense about attendance procedures.

Mr. Tozer got our attention merely by walking on the stage of the theater-in-the-round, where these reunions were held. His normally cheerful face was morose, his posture defeated.

Still we were somewhat hostile. The coach next to me muttered, "This better be good, goddammit. I've got work to do."

"I've called this meeting to inform you of a tragedy that happened to one of our kids yesterday. I think it's important to deal with this with your students, since stories and rumors will be circulating."

Most minds were racing, trying to second-guess his message. Had someone been burned in an accident and we should talk about safety? Was there a new wave of drugs, pregnancies, runaways? Some braced themselves secretly, hoping it would not be about someone they knew.

"Yesterday afternoon Peter Lorenzo left school, apparently distraught about a math test, put a twenty-two-caliber gun to his temple, and killed himself."

No one breathed.

"I've already had a conference with the parents, at their request, this morning. They want to impress upon all of Peter's teachers not to blame themselves."

There was no sound in the room save the click of the government-issue clock. Everyone just sat there.

"There is a large concern on the part of the parents that the other two Lorenzo children be able to deal with the curiosity of their peers. Perhaps you can help out by explaining, if that's possible, what happened."

There were some scattered affirmative nods. Some resented the inconvenience and showed it. I saw a math teacher crying.

"I think we're dealing once again with a higher truth than just subject matter. Peter's self-esteem was on the line. He obviously hated himself to the point of destruction. We need to constantly reassess our role with kids. There is a whole person there whose needs should be our concern."

On the subject of our principal, we were a divided staff. Mr. Tozer was not the average "chief at the helm aboard the ship of education." More the anarchist chaplain. He was the unlikely combination of a liberal, humanitarian, Republican Mormon with a preference for magic tricks, a proclivity toward homilies, a wonderful singing voice, and an unabashed love of children. He talked to teachers all the time about noticing kids, seeing more than the name on the paper, feeling out where the student was emotionally, learning something from him, or sharing a bad joke.

Losers, cruisers, boozers, jocks, socies, lowriders, ornery cusses, whiny fussers, handicapped, stoned, streetwise, or stupid—he found something of value in each kid. The P. E. Department thought he was a "puss"; Science wished he'd be more structured; Humanities loved his gentleness; Math found him obtuse; Fine Arts wanted him for governor. Most kids wished he were their father.

He was fired. The school board reasoned he was weak and did not place enough emphasis on football.

The bell rang. An eerie silence followed us to our rooms. I had Peter's brother in class, a bright, sensitive boy who loved physics and pistons with equal ardor. He also loved Peter; he'd spoken of him so many times in class. How he protected Peter because he wasn't smart, how he was awed by Peter's daring on a motocycle, and how much he relished their into-the-night chats in their too-small bedroom of the tract house they both hated.

I found myself fixating on what mindless rituals teachers are asked to perform in the name of education. Taking roll, checking lesson plans, passing out Driver-Education forms.

It's no wonder most students think teachers never notice them beyond a function for a mark. There is some reality basis to that.

Three of Peter's teachers did not know who he was.

Happily, the majority clearly does not operate like that. The system makes us look like impersonal guardians of pedagogical nonsense, but most of us have inner tapes running at breakneck speed.

Most teachers experience a dualistic dialogue on automatic pilot:

LEVEL I: "Billy, will you please stop bugging Joyce."

LEVEL II: "If someone shaved my head like that, I'd be pissy too."

The wall between us and the students is blessed by the state, sanctioned by the home, reinforced by the rules, built higher by myth, thicker by bluff—and yet, the facade is made of sunny cellophane. Each side never really loses sight of the other.

We notice them.

They notice us.

We do not get to talk about it.

❦ ❦ ❦

A Local Habitation and a Name

Twenty years ago, the Southern California terrain from Los Angeles to the Mexican border was composed of sleepy agricultural hamlets boasting of thriving Rotary Clubs, 4-H groups, and country fairs. Signs like POINSETTIA CAPITAL OF THE WORLD peppered the two-lane highway snaking its way south past the occasional exit to communities of affluence like La Jolla or Rancho Santa Fe, kept politically gerrymandered and ethnically pure by gentlemen's agreements in real estate.

Small towns were created by clusters of upwardly mobile middle-class families looking for suburban comfort and space for patios with built-in barbecues.

Schools were small, provincial institutions offering courses in animal husbandry. Fairly innocent childhoods were spent cruising main streets from the Dairy Queen to the Jack-in-the-Box, or hanging out at Friday night football games.

Summers were lived on the beach. The Pump House Gang was down the road.

There was no smog or heavy traffic.

Most people shared similar values. Those who didn't lived in old houses in Laguna or Del Mar, dabbled in creative jobs, and were called bohemians.

The largest local controversy was the banning of an Elvis Presley concert on moral grounds.

I returned to this area in the fall of 1970, after years of roaming Europe trying to reconcile the events of the sixties with the lure of the future. Two decisions had been reached concerning living with the system: I would return to teaching relevant subjects, and my husband would enter law school.

We would deal with issues at the core; however, practicality had to come first. I had to find a job.

The teachers' market was glutted with overeducated, underexperienced idealists in search of a forum. All the metropolitan districts had long lists of anxious substitutes and no foreseeable openings.

I couldn't even get an interview.

In a fit of exaggerated self-pity, I called my high school district and asked for an appointment with the director of personnel who, as it turned out, had taught me to drive fifteen years earlier on those country roads that were now major highways with numbers for names.

He remembered me. So did some of the others, and by some fluke of alumni nepotism, I was offered a job.

The school looked the same from the outside, but all

similarities to my past had been swamped by the sprawlingly self-conscious affluence surrounding the building.

What were once tomato fields used for after-dance parking sessions were now rows of prefabricated Taras with fake marble tile entryways, microwave ovens, and garage doors that opened from a flick of a button in a luxury automobile. Streets wound up and down freshly graded hills, sporting names like Willowdale Avenue and Levante Lane. In the midst of arid vegetation and succulents, man-made lakes stood like mirages offering waterfront-view homes with private docks to those families able to come up with a higher down payment.

Flocks of Los Angeles city dwellers, weary from freeway tie-ups, migrated south in search of what they saw as a rural experience.

New industries blossomed, from nuclear power plants to ecological control systems.

Several universities sprang up, and scores of diehards from the Yankee coast immigrated west in search of academic advancement, an easier lifestyle, a little bit of sunshine, while still retaining the arrogant assumption that they brought the culture with them.

Naval officers opted for a more spacious environment and bought tract homes near Miramar and Camp Pendleton.

Beach people now owned inordinately valuable property and the rhetoric of Red Carpet Real Estate became the local lingo. Homes were now "investments" and "foils against inflation." The Mexican barrios became expensive housing even for the continuous flow of illegal aliens who worked in the fields.

Shopping malls mushroomed ominously.

Religions whose names I could not pronounce flourished and disappeared as quickly as morning glories.

Nobody's parents had the same last name as the children.

The student parking lot was filled with Porsches, BMWs, XKEs, and lowriders. Everyone strangled on prepositions.

"He's *into* heavy metal."

"She's *between* jobs."

"He's *out* of it."

"I'll get *behind* it."

I was a stranger in a strange land. Even the colleagues who were once my teachers had metamorphosed.

The former ROTC instructor wore Bongo shirts and love beads.

My favorite biology teacher was "into" Maslow's Hierarchy of Needs, the art teacher had turned Trotskyite, P. E. was trying to incorporate holistic exercise, and the English Department now offered courses called Rock Poetry, Epistemics, Values Clarification, and Journal Writing.

I never heard grammar mentioned.

I was the wallflower at the orgy.

My job was to teach the underachievers at two separate schools—fifteen minutes apart in distance and light years apart in philosophical orientation. I had to change my personal philosophy during the hasty commute.

At the high school, I was required to be loose, open, to go

with the flow until the child felt ready to respond to learning. Smoke breaks and spontaneous overflows to free-form hostility were to be regarded as growth-producing. Precisely whose was never quite clear. I was a facilitator of education, not a leader; a presence whose wishes were supposed to vibrate frontal lobes with a thirst for questioning.

The junior high was the antithesis of free thought. An autocratic demon with an inviolate sense of Napoleonic law ruled this domain with an iron fist. I was to be twice as tough with the underachievers, since they were losers who "belong in trade schools anyway." He insisted we mark tardies, write up slips for insubordination, and crack down on the scourge of sensitivity groups. The teacher next door to me was violent with his students. He was praised for running a tight ship.

I began to understand schizophrenigenicity. External forces can make people crazy.

Each system was extreme, one-dimensional, and ultimately foolish. But the kids were the same—discouraged, void of basic skills, lacking self-esteem, and completely missing some sane kind of adult guidance. In the midst of all that chaos, I formulated a point of view that allowed me to go on with what I saw as my job.

I tightened up at the high school and insisted they try my way. Their turn would come later.

I gave them a turn at the junior high.

Somehow it worked out.

I don't accept the term *loser;* kids who can't read and write are disadvantaged. Avalanches of unconditional love or death grips of structure don't teach skills. Somewhere in between is the reasonable terrain where work has to take place on both sides.

When the rules were clear, we did just fine.

And I became the "losers' teacher."

Every underachiever in the school was sent to me for overhauling, like a favorite car temporarily on the fritz. I resented that, though I loved those kids. I was creating some women's studies courses, since the subject interested me on many levels and was not being taught in any form.

The response from the community was indicative of the socioeconomic breakdown.

The young moderns who lived near tennis courts and health spas felt Women's Studies was a welcome addition as long as it stuck to the economic issues (equal pay for equal work).

The religious fanatics complained bitterly and quoted St. Paul as they yanked their children from the class, howling about the undermining of the family unit.

The university consultants wanted to verify that I had included a Marxist framework.

The Chicano community thought it was crazy to teach about women.

So did three fourths of my male colleagues.

A core of families was wonderfully encouraging. They offered books, records, guest lectures, slide shows, and personal anecdotes.

It was an invigorating time for me, although I became the

"women's libber" museum curio and listened to endlessly tiresome diatribes on the subject from every conceivable point of view.

Then more houses were built for an increasingly wealthy influx of defectors from other states, eager to begin anew in the land of recreated personas and habitual rebeginnings.

Bevies of lath-and-plaster estates with Spanish-style roofs, three-car garages, built-in everythings, and upgraded carpets and drapes attracted thousands of "professionals."

La Costa became the ultimate spa for overweight dowagers, frazzled movie stars, and anyone with ennui and a lot of money.

Golf tournaments and tennis matches called national attention to what was once open space devoid of interest.

Families demanded more academic excellence, including honors courses, programs for the mentally gifted and more capable learners. This coterie became vocal and effective.

A job opened up to coordinate a program and teach one of the subjects. I applied out of curiosity, not to mention a raging desire to hear a student say "I did well" instead of "I did good," and to be able to discuss literature.

I had no idea what the committee sought in terms of qualifications, but the makeup of the group amused and horrified me.

My judges were the following: my principal, whom I loved for his vulnerability; a school board member who I always suspected wanted to chuck his insurance business and ride off on a Harley-Davidson; a mother from the fundamentalist group who firmly supported the Lord's will; a physics whiz kid obsessed with *Star Trek* and black holes; and a former AFT agitator turned corporate lackey.

I have no memory of what they asked or what I answered. I do remember the sun glaring fiercely off a crucifix dangling from Mrs. Jones's ample bosom, which I took as a bad omen.

I got the job and overnight became known as the "winners' teacher." My phone rang off the hook with calls such as: "If you could only see the myth my Johnny wrote in second grade, you'd *know* he's gifted."

My mailbox overflowed with samples of "exceptional intelligence." I still don't know what *gifted* means. I suspect we're all gifted somewhere and that school merely reinforces some of us.

The classes were filled in a matter of days. Row upon row of blond, tan, high verbals poured into the Humanities seminars. I had no luck recruiting Chicanos. The state law mandated an IQ test as the qualifier. All of these tests are in English and ask questions like "What are galoshes?"

The program has been successful. We've received a lot of press attention. Most of the kids are in good colleges, doing good work; in short, they are winners.

And so, happily, are some of the losers.

The vast majority of those in the middle are doing all right too.

I want to believe I have made a difference to some of them.

Days pass uneventfully much of the time. The lull of the

mundane in a teacher's life has a certain rhythm regardless of locale. Rituals must be followed, rules observed or broken, motion divided by bells.

Yet there are special spaces where lives collide, away from freeways and flower fields, systems and sociograms.

In these corners, Mrs. Kamali can talk about Cloud.

Juicy Brucie, or Take Me to the Drive-in

The little theater was sectioned off pielike to accommodate the avalanche of new kids. I had one quarter of the stage as a "dish," with plastic dividers on either side, keeping my American Novel class away from Drama I on the left and Vehicle-Code Summary on the right.

We literally had to outshout the Verse Choir's rendition of something about the Big Mississippi and Lake Titicaca. No-left-turns-on-red-lights made no noise.

The class was a curious mixture of reading levels, interests, and reasons for being in there in the first place.

"I love the Gatsby look."

"I have always admired Tolstoy."

"I hear you're a cruise."

"Nothing else was open."

"I hate biology."

We started out the semester with *The Scarlet Letter.* I

gave them a rundown on life in Puritan America. It never ceases to amaze me how much everyone likes to be talked to. It's an adult version of story time. The kids were obsessed by the rigid sexual codes imposed on their ancestors. The origin of the word *fuck* made them laugh, then grow pensive.

I overheard two drill-team members discussing the stocks.

"Half of this fucking school would be in stocks if they got busted for unlawful carnal knowledge."

"Jo Anne Myers would spend her life there. If it moves, she screws it."

"That's the wonder of the Pill. Hester coulda been saved a lot of headaches."

We got some good discussions out of the saga of the adulteress. Most of the group thought Hester was "a slut who got what she deserved." The girls tended to think Dimmesdale was a "lowdown hypocrite who didn't admit that it takes two to tango." Everybody liked Pearl, the rebellious free child who spat on governors; she rang a sympathetic chord in all of them.

I wondered what it would be like if Hawthorne came back and heard love children of the seventies talking about his art.

"That Chillyworth asshole is a bad dude."

"Wouldn't you wipe some guy's ass who screwed your wife, man?"

"I think you guys should remember that he left Hester while he went curing Indians. If a man puts his career before his family, I say Hester gets to do what she wants."

"You're a slut too if you feel like that."

I felt an obligation at this point to express my personal feelings on inappropriate speech. No one really listened.

"Well, I feel like Hester got a raw deal. It isn't easy being a single mother, you know."

"Dimmesdale shoulda told his parish to accept him as a real person. Real people love and make babies."

I risked a feminist interpretation of Hester as victim of a rigidly sexist society. The next day I found a brightly sequined letter A in my mailbox. The culprit turned out to be a female exchange student who thought I admired Hester too much. She confessed on the last day of school by writing her cathartic message in my yearbook.

We had just begun *The Red Badge of Courage* in my American Novel class. The students were supposed to read at grade level and have had a college-prep background in order to enroll. The counselor's job was to screen kids beforehand. The system had frequent flaws.

I was reading some of Crane's poetry when Brucie walked in. A more apt verb here would be "swaggered." He was a handsome boy—tan, broad white smile, enormous shoulders, and swimming-pool eyes. It took me a minute to realize that he wasn't wearing a shirt and that both his hands were stuck down the front of his pants.

I must admit I have a painful bias. Men who touch themselves, absentmindedly or on purpose, in my presence make me anxious.

The kids in the class were silent. The girls were going crazy with secret signals of, Check out this one, Libby. I tried to look unruffled.

"You the teacher?"

He eyed me up and down with a leer I thought was confined to singles bars and sleazy hotels.

"Yes. I'm Mrs. Martin." Casting all feminist doctrine aside, I hit hard on the Mrs.

"Oh yeah."

He picked up on it immediately.

"Yes. How may I help you?"

His eyes were on my nipples.

"You don't look married."

"Are you supposed to be in here?"

His hands drifted around in his jeans. "I'm new. By the way, I want you to know that I like older women."

"Wonderful. Sit down."

He stared at my breasts again. "Where?"

"Anywhere you can find a seat."

He raised his eyebrows and snuck a look at my ass.

"Hurry up, Mr. ? . . ."

"Harding. Bruce Harding."

He hit heavy on the Hard.

The girls noticed that one, and a few giggled.

"Please take your chair, Mr. Harding."

In order to make this plausible, I will relate exactly, in detail, what happened next.

He took both hands out of his pants.

He smiled a hebephrenic grin.

He bent over to touch his palms to the floor, rose to a perfect handstand, and walked on his hands with agility and grace until he reached the empty seat.

Standing upside down, but perfectly still, he lowered himself to a bend, stood up, smiled, put his hands back in his groin, and sat down.

I don't know what I said, but the other kids clapped.

Bruce rose, took a bow, and sat down.

"That's quite impressive, Mr. Harding. Are you a gymnast?"

"Yeah, but gettin' a teacher is tough. All the women want me, all the guys get jealous."

"I see. Well, why don't you stay a minute after class so I can give you a book and get you organized."

"See? You too! Pretty soon it'll be after school, after dinner, whaddya bet?"

"Don't hold your breath."

I resumed reading Crane's poetry to the class. They were only mildly interested.

I tried to wake them with a question. "What's fatalism?" I got no answer.

"What is a fatalistic point of view?"

"When you think life is fucked," Brucie said.

Basically he was right.

"Could you give us an example, cleaning up your language so I don't lose my job if some administrator walks in?"

"Fatalism is when your father drinks too much and everyone knows, so you don't care if you find bottles in the bathroom," a girl in the corner offered.

"The bathroom. Ha, reminds me. I gotta take a leak," Bruce brayed.

I've never much cared for the idea that people should ask permission to urinate, but somehow I felt that I'd never see this guy again if he just left.

"Would you like a pass?"

I never use passes; my students knew it and looked at me funny.

"Pass, my ass. I gotta bleed my lizard."

In a flash he'd flipped upside down and galloped out the door, on his hands, not faltering an instant.

"Follow him, Roland. If he pees upside down, we'll send it to 'Ripley's Believe It or Not.' "

Roland came back in five minutes. "I can't find him anywhere."

I knew it.

The term *in loco parentis* oozed its way into my head. Translated, that means if he gets in trouble, I'm responsible. I pay his doctor bills, I get sued for neglect.

Three minutes after the last bell rang, Brucie popped up in my room. I was clearing off a table when I looked up. He was poised like Andrianov, his head tilted, proud and arrogant. He took a running start to a cartwheel, a roundoff, and a back somersault, landing perfectly still on two booted feet.

"Pretty bitchin', huh?"

"Actually, you're quite terrific. Where the hell did you go?"

"I was in the gym with Miss Riley. She wants me."

His grin was beginning to unsettle me, and his hands were poised on the waistband of his white shorts.

"Miss Riley will have to confirm that for me."

"She'll never admit she wants me, because of that asshole overseas she's waiting for. She's so horny for me it's pathetic."

"I agree something here is pathetic."

Miss Riley was the girls' P. E. teacher, the ultimate California Dream Girl, tan, blond, toothy, healthy, perky, athletic, hard-working, and deeply religious. In short, I could not stand her or her endless testimonials to Jesus, prayers before games, witnessing to Jewish students, or her barrage of "far outs," "reallys," "for sures," and "not too shabbys."

"She's been after my ass for a week."

"How many days have you been here?"

"What do you care?"

"Bruce, have you had any American Lit before?"

"I had the teacher. She got me to come in a Dixie cup."

"How nice for you. Why do you talk such shit?" I was genuinely curious by now.

"Love's not shit; mellow in."

"This conversation makes no sense at all."

"You looking for meaning?"

"Truth, for starters. What is your story?"

"Would you like to kiss me?"

"Not much."

He pointed his toes in fourth position, did two full tournés, a back walkover to a straddle roll out the door.

I charged the attendance office to look up his schedule. He was registered in six classes. I checked him out with my colleagues the next morning.

"Miss Riley, do you know Bruce Harding?"

"For sure."

"What's his story?"

"He's a gymnast from Monterey High. Did the rings for the varsity."

"Mr. Pottery, is Bruce Harding in your chemistry class?"

"Sort of. He monkeys around the lab too much on his hands, but he tells me he won the Science Fair at Fresno High."

"Herr Young, is this Bruce Harding kid in your German class?"

"Ja. His father was stationed in Heidelberg last year."

One last bastion of information was the nurse. Since she had no power whatsoever to treat anything, she lovingly gave teachers access to the files. There wasn't a thing on him.

"Julie, do you know this Bruce Harding kid?"

"I put tape on his ankle last week."

"What is it with that kid?"

"He's just disappointed because he had to quit Martha Graham's troupe when they moved from New York. He practices in the gym."

I confronted him the next week.

"Bruce, where are you from?"

"I know where I'd like to go."

"Where?" (Mistake.)

"To the drive-in, with you."

"Why do you do this?" (The question was genuine.)

"If I had you in the backseat, I'd love you up like you've never had it before. I have some special treats I'm good at."

"What, pray tell, are those?" (I *had* to hear.)

He told me.

I would be lying if I said his suggestions didn't intrigue me. Excite me. Puzzle me.

"Bruce, where are your parents?"

He was in a backbend now.

No answer.

"Where are you from?"

Over to the splits, up to a perfect pike. "Will you give me a ride home?"

Jumping at the chance to play detective, I said yes. I lured him to the parking lot, where he did a cartwheel before climbing into my car.

He had me circling the same territory like a crazed buzzard.

His hands raced up and down my thigh despite protests, slaps, and threats.

"Stop here!"

I did. It was a nondescript street corner. I felt battle weary, bored, and agitated.

"Thanks for the ride. I'll repay you, Teach."

"Just do your work and stop driving us nuts in class."

He smiled that appealingly dreadful grin and put his

hands down his pants. I stiffened ever so slightly and stared at the stop sign until I heard the first sob. Big tears rolled down his face. Salty-sad, spleen-dribbled droplets.

"I can't read at all. Not at all."

He jumped out the door. Before I could unfasten my seat belt he was gone. I drove around, but I didn't find him.

None of us ever did.

I have a fantasy about the Moscow Olympics in 1980. I confess to a shameful idolatry of Nadia Comaneci, Olga Korbut, and the rest. I want to be in a Russian hotel room with a color television. My love and I will be eating imported Jamoca Almond Fudge ice cream and watching the gymnastics finals. Russia and America are tied for first place.

Andrianov gets a 9.75 on the floor. The crowd waits for the American to topple him.

Brucie skips up, smiles to the judges, and does a knockout routine to the music from *The Sting.* He twirls and twists, flips and spins, in a dazzling tour de force of grace and loveliness. The crowd goes crazy. A perfect 10 lights up the scoreboard.

He's called to the platform for his gold medal. Bends to receive it, smiles that grin that shakes all dreamers loose, and puts his hands discreetly on the waistband of his warmups, just below the elastic.

Princess Grace

The high school definition of pretty is certainly subject to historical alteration. I can remember when Tammy Wynette look-alikes with eyeliner caused tremors, when sack-dressed little Suzis won hearts and football heroes. I have seen the rewards bestowed upon big chests, flat chests, Twiggies, Farrahs, and freaks. The late sixties I'm-more-working-class-than-you-are dress-down-chic provided an arena where homely-pretty Barbra Streisands would succeed, even shine. The shake-down sixties gave birth to the high-rise seventies, when terms like *grooming, styled, tapered, blow-dried,* and *makeup* no longer implied defection to the other side.

Sometimes it's frightening to contemplate what that represents in terms of conspicuous consumption. No one wears the same outfit more than once a month. I spy shoes, purses, jewelry, and clothes on my students that make the best-dressed secretary look like something out of Pic 'n' Save.

In short, we are back to the cult of the queen bee syndrome—the coiffed young Edwardian, tasteful, stick-pinned, leather-booted beauty princess who coordinates a persona. In a moment of extreme boredom, one day I borrowed a student's calculator to estimate the net worth of the threads of my thirty-some-odd students. The conservative estimate was fifty-five hundred dollars, including shoes.

There is always one whose radiant beauty transcends all fads and fancies, bypasses organic surfer sylphs and frizzed-out femmes fatales. She is the ultimate physical embodiment of aesthetic perfection. And she knows it.

Such was Ariel, clearly a girl to be savored from afar. Not only was she captivating, she was rich, charming, intelligent, poised, polite, and aloof. An aura of mystery surrounded her, precisely because it was not cultivated. Her teachers noticed it. Fellow students noticed it.

On some level, every male in her periphery was in love with her. She was the quintessence of the unattainable other.

I had to cajole Ariel into taking my class. She was certified by the state as a mentally gifted minor. A dubious honor that roughly meant she had an IQ above 132 on the Stanford-Binet, an affluent family, pushy parents, good reading habits, or all of the above.

She had never opted for the Honors Humanities Seminar and I wanted to know why. At this point I only knew her by her records. She was a "good" student in "good" classes, which "good" universities loved to read on "good" transcripts. I couldn't understand how she could steer clear of my scintillating discourses on Dostoyevsky. She was quite cool about it when I asked her.

"Oh, I just never thought of it in terms of being different from what I'm doing now."

I knew all about her previous English class, and I sizzled with the idea of being compared to a colleague I considered a mediocre flake, at best. It was a matter of pride, no question there; but her passive control unnerved me.

"Will you think about it for next semester?" I asked, suddenly conscious of my grammar, my manners, and my appearance.

"I'll check and see if I can fit it in without too much rearranging."

She did not smile; she thanked me for taking my time to seek her out. I studied her as she walked off to buy a can of V-8 Juice, which, as I came to find out, was her lunch.

Her hair fell nearly to her waist in smooth auburn waves. Her figure was svelte and graceful. Her face had even features that were all the more intriguing for her lack of commitment to an expression. It wasn't exaggerated patience; she simply was not involved.

She took the class. She never missed an assignment, but she missed class two days a week. She always had a "legitimate excuse," that is to say an official sanction from the front office, which isn't saying much. I never sign those things. One well-kept secret of my off-the-wall methodology is that I teach my students how to forge my signature the first day of school.

I loathe details.

They know it and don't blow me in.

I do, however, notice when kids are gone. I most certainly was aware when Ariel was gone, because the entire class acted differently. People felt freer to act out, talk louder, cruder, and longer. As I write this, I realize the implication of that observation.

She had the control.

I did not.

Correct.

We were doing Vance Packard's *Status Seekers.* I asked all the kids to list the status symbols of their world. The results were telling.

O. P. shorts and Hansen Surf Boards for the surfed-out, sun-bleached urchins.

Hot cars, mainly GTOs, and slick clothes from Contempo, The Gap, or Judy's.

Ariel's list included Giorgio's, Gucci, Godiva chocolates, Rolls-Royce Corniches, Häagen-Dazs ice cream, foreign films, and little-known resorts listed by country.

My list for my peer group covered day-care centers, Volvos, BMWs, cork wines, and Cuisinart food processers.

I asked her about the L. A. haunts, since most of my students never left the beach, and thought high culture was an avocado-and-sprout sandwich on whole-grain bread.

"Did you used to live in L. A.?"

"No."

"How do you know these places?"

"I visit."

That thought intrigued me because my husband and I have long been L.A. freaks. The two-hour drive is easy. We go spend weekends seeing five movies a day and eating. Our relatives, friends, and coworkers think we're crazy. I've given up trying to explain why to anyone. Ariel understood immediately.

We questioned each other about films, places, restaurants, and dives. She knew them all. Her face lit up a bit when she spoke of it.

The next day she was gone. She came back with an excuse. I asked no questions.

My last words to my classes on Fridays are always "Go to the movies." I do not understand their obsession with reality. I give them a rundown on what's playing where. I am a shameless celluloid junkie, I go four times a week.

Ariel stayed after my Friday class. She needed to ask me something about an exam next week. I screamed at the stragglers to go see *Outrageous* and shut the door.

"Mrs. Martin." She never called me by my first name as most of the students did.

"Yes, Ariel?"

I was aware of lapsing into the formal.

"What should I do about the test next week? I won't be here."

It was a direct statement, not an apology.

"Why don't you take it the day before?"

I did not ask her where she was going. I would have, had it been another student.

"Is that okay with you, then?"

She was verifying.

"Yes."

She named a well-known film and asked me if I liked it.

"Yes, the director was fascinating," I felt compelled to footnote.

"I know him."

"Oh. Well, he's certainly a gifted director."

"Have you ever heard anything about his former wife?"

"Sure."

"What happened to her?"

Sensing my age next to a girl who could not possibly relate to that era, I reran my mental obituaries to get my facts straight. "She killed herself."

"Was it an accident?"

"I don't really know."

"Was she beautiful?"

"I thought she was classy."

"Oh."

I couldn't resist one question. "How do you know him?"

"I met him at a golf tournament in L. A."

"Oh."

"Well, I'll see you. Thanks for your understanding."

I did not understand a thing.

She was gone again Monday. I checked her admit slip. Orthodontist appointment.

She smiled up at me Tuesday morning: "I always say that."

"Hasn't anyone ever noticed that you don't have braces?"

A cool, ironic smile curled the corners of her lips. "No way. I've never been asked any questions."

There was a silent warning in her tone of voice. I heeded it.

We discussed Caroline Bird's *Born Female.* The class was asked to estimate the yearly economic worth of a housewife.

"Housewives don't get paid."

"Right, stupid. That's what you're supposed to conclude."

"Do we include a chauffeur's fee?"

"How much do women charge for watching soap operas?"

"Shut up, asshole."

"Housewives don't do a thing, and they get everything free."

Ariel traced the culprit who ventured that one. "You always work for what you get."

The boy reddened immediately and returned to his calculations. The class fell silent.

Ariel flipped her hair back in a quick snap of her head. I noticed a diamond pendant on a chain around her neck. Elegant, tasteful, and costly.

"Is this class a Women's Lib meeting? This book is boring."

"Why don't girls just marry money?"

"I think Barbara Walters is fairly paid, don't you?"

"I'm sick of male oppression!"

"I'm sick of you and that fuckin' patchouli oil you drown us in, hippie."

"Shut your face, capitalist."

Mercifully, the bell rang.

Ariel remained seated until the room was empty and we were alone.

"I can't take your test Thursday. Plans have changed."

"What plans?" I was slightly annoyed at her directness, but still curious to hear her answer.

"I have to go to L.A. on Thursday, so I can't take the makeup."

"Then take it Friday with the rest of the class."

"I can't."

"Why not?"

"I'm busy."

Either courage or masochism mustered the next question.

"Ariel, without invading your privacy, would you please tell me precisely what's going on here?"

She studied me for a minute, making her discomfort at being put on the spot subtle but clear.

"I have to be in L. A. again."

"Do you drive up there twice a week?"

"No. I fly."

Mental calculations of air fare rattled in my head. She guessed it.

"My savings are being depleted; however, it's a question of priorities."

"What do you do in L. A. that is so terribly urgent?"

I was aware of how badly I had worded that question.

"I see my friend. It's expensive, but it's worth it. Taxis from the airport cost as much as the air fare."

I digested this information without emotion.

"Ariel, do you know what you're doing?"

"You mean about school?"

"That's not what I mean at all."

"Yeah. I worry about delayed schedules sometimes, but I'm always home for dinner."

I did not ask if her parents knew about this. I knew her high school friends did not. On some level she was trusting me with it and I felt a responsibility there. Without thinking, I posed the next question.

"Ariel, are you on the Pill?"

She didn't change expression.

"Yes."

"Do you trust this man?"

"Yes."

"Do you know that if you are caught he is in a great deal of legal trouble?"

"Yes."

"Ariel, be careful. These things can hurt more than one person."

She sighed a well mulled over "I know."

We talked about it cautiously. How they'd met. Why she liked him, how out of place she felt with her peers, how cleverly she got away with it. That I understood. I admit to an uncanny attraction toward risk takers who pull off stunts of daring under public scrutiny. We even laughed about logistics. But I was slightly uneasy.

"Did you ever consider how easy it would be to be a CIA agent?"

I confessed that I had entertained that fantasy, despite the negative press on the subject.

"Do you love this man, Ariel?"

"He loves me."

"That's not what I asked."

"I don't know."

"What happens next year when you're in college?"

"He wants me to live with him."

"What do you want?"

"I have my own plans for university and graduate school."

"Does he know this?"

"Sort of."

"Be careful, Ariel, not to let the situation get out of hand."

"I know."

She gathered up her books in her Gucci satchel that I'd never noticed until then.

"I'll keep your secret."

"Thanks."

She missed Thursday and Friday. Another orthodontist appointment appeared on her Monday admit slip. We exchanged conspiratorial smiles. I didn't really approve of all of this, but my uneasiness masqueraded as tolerance. She was gone the following Wednesday of every week until May. We never spoke of it at all. She did her work, held the class in order, and made plans for college. She chose Princeton.

I was surprised.

She dropped into class in June. She stayed after one very hot Santa Ana afternoon.

"He's been calling my house."

"Can you talk to him?"

"No, my mom is always around."

"Does she ever answer the phone?"

"Yes. I tell her it's my chemistry teacher asking about labs. I'm his aide."

"What does he want, Ariel?"

"Me."

"You've been avoiding L. A. for a while?"

"Sometimes I wonder if I have any feelings."

"Why do you say that?"

"Because I don't want to destroy another person."

I helped her put on her cap and gown. Women faculty members were always assigned that job. I wanted to hug her, but I was afraid. She looked like a Christmas tree angel, blending in perfectly with the other excited faces. She marched in unison to the flashes of Kodaks and a slightly off-key "Pomp and Circumstance."

I saw him on television this summer. He's a nice-looking man, very charming, with lovely laughing eyes.

A box of Godiva chocolates arrived from Bullock's. Beautiful sea shells, tennis rackets, and semisweet mermaids filled the gold box. I thought my husband had sent them as a gift.

The card was simple and tasteful.

Melody Martin ✧ ✧ ✧

I'm on my way to Europe. Have been in New York at the Plaza. I want to live here some time.

Thank you for everything.

Ariel

He is promoting a new film in the United States that is getting rave reviews. She is in Europe visiting museums and fancy hotels before starting Princeton.

Her parents are at home, delightedly sharing postcards of her travels with family friends.

I am rereading *Sentimental Education* and wondering if these star-crossed lovers are still together.

The Paraquat Papers

At least it's not like the sixties, when every other adolescent regardless of group had a stash in his locker. The drug problem, as school officials are fond of labeling it, has slackened off a bit in favor of alcohol, a problem these same officials seem to ignore.

Dope is still everywhere, but the magnitude of usage has changed. During the Vietnam war every teenager's vocabulary was peppered with words like *reds, ups, downers, turn arounders, grass, weed, acid, peyote,* and *pot.* A trip was something you took in a friend's van on Saturday night without starting the ignition. Wandering joint carriers roamed the halls offering not-so-discreet "hits" to interested students. Overdoses on high school campuses were commonplace. Drug education programs cautiously crept into the curriculum. The early educational materials were laughable. Films like *Today the Joint, Tomorrow the Needle* brought howls of stoned laughter.

I remember being invited to a "screening" of one such film by a sympathetic colleague. It was intended to be a hip message—not preachy, just informative—about the dangers of LSD. It proved to be neither. Acid heads were shown to be psychopaths in the style of Charles Manson, ready to commit heinous crimes against innocent victims. The smart refusers were portrayed as hip Ricky Nelsons whose inner strength to resist dangerous drugs was rewarded by blondes, dune buggies, and jobs in self-help clinics. (Football heroes were irrelevant by then.)

Any reasonable message got so garbled in didactic *Reader's Digest* prose that the film actually made drug use appealing by comparison.

Which is too bad.

There weren't many teenage Aldous Huxleys created by taking acid. If anything, there were tragedies when fragile kids attempted cosmic consciousness via the chemical implosion.

In the late sixties pills became a medium of social exchange, money, a passport to friends or popularity, and a status symbol of social prowess.

Alcohol has usurped that position in the late seventies. Students know the difference between a Piña Colada and a Tequila Sunrise. Beer is bought by label, hard liquor is consumed in the proper glasses. I have heard informative exchanges on the merits of California wines versus French imports from fourteen-year-olds. Prom dates are fueled by

Rob Roys and Margaritas. The organics mix the latter with real lime and natural sea salt.

Only the magic herbs remain omnipresent, but now marijuana is identified by cut, plant, potency, and country of origin.

"I have some excellent highland Colombian, no seeds."

The average high school student's botanical fact sheet vis à vis altered states of consciousness would astound the average biology teacher as well as those parents of the average student who are convinced that no one learns anything anymore. They do indeed; right down to the correct properties and life phenomena.

Cannabis: say that word out loud in front of a group of kids. Someone will ask you if you have any.

Dubie asked me the first time I ever laid eyes on him. He was standing in front of me, worming his way into an imitation Beatles band assembly sponsored by the Associated Student Body. I was to chaperone the southwest door, for what I was never told.

He was taller than I, and I guessed him to be about fifteen. His light brown hair curled all over his head like unbraided rope. He bounced along, singing a Pink Floyd atrocity, shaking his head to keep the beat. His left hand, clenching a geometry book, moved back and forth to his solo festival. The crowd shoved from behind. I was heaved forward and the binding of the geometry book hit me on the breast. I recoiled in pain. He saw it happen and flinched with me.

"Are they all right?"

"What do you mean 'they'?"

"Whaddya want me to call them—Gladys?"

The wound still stung, but my dignity was rattled more.

"Sorry, lady, really . . . you got any weed?"

"It's okay, and no, I don't."

"What's your name?"

"Martin."

"You work here?"

"Alas!"

"I'm Dubie Wexler."

He handed me a card.

FOSTER "DUBIE" WEXLER
Professional Amateur
Sex, Drugs, Alcohol
"it's only rock 'n' roll"
(555-8235)

I thanked him automatically. We were edging our way closer to the door now. His name was vaguely familiar.

"Whaddya teach?"

"The gifted . . ."

"You're the bitch who called my stepfather! I'm not takin' your fucking class with those fucking geeks that he thinks are superior because they follow fascist doctrines of social order. I hope your tit gets cancer."

I thought I'd been transposed in time. It had been five years since I had heard the word *fascist,* and that was in Berkeley.

He tried to forge ahead, but he was stuck in the crowd.

"You're a hostile little creep, aren't you, Groovy Dubie?"

"I think, therefore I am weird."

"And pretentious to boot."

I was suitably impressed that he knew about Descartes.

"The masses are asses."

Ditto for Twain.

"Traditional education is a nonorgasmic fuck."

He was insightful.

"Relive 1968. Riot at a convention."

Informed.

"Give me Librium or give me meth."

I spoke up here. "You're a real pain in the ass, aren't you?"

He howled the words to "Blowin' in the Wind" while other kids looked on in disbelief.

"Later, Martin. Call my stepfather again and I'll put plutonium on your plugs."

He was swallowed up in the crowd. I took my stinging boob to the southwest door and stationed myself there trying to find him. I did not succeed. I tried to remember who his stepfather was. I tried to let the whole incident be washed away by phony renditions of "Sgt. Pepper's Lonely Hearts Club Band."

Some days later I think I was droning on about Raskolnikov when I saw the curly head pass by the window. "Anarchy to the masses!"

He got everyone's attention by staying at the window.

"It's just Dubie doper," someone said.

"Yeah. He's probably stoned again."

"Revolution now!" He was center stage again and we all turned to look.

"Violate imperialist tyranny!"

A National Merit Scholar flipped him off.

"Fuck you, asshole, you'll be working for the nuclear race in Kansas someday and I'll be plotting your demise!"

I walked outside to ask him to leave. He was wearing a Rocky Horror T-shirt and carrying his backpack slung over one shoulder.

"Don't these cretins depress you, man?"

I made a mistake and smiled. He moved in closer.

"Wanna get high?"

"Not especially."

I looked at his eyes. The whites were red, the pupils down to slits; the lids twitched with a regular rhythm.

"Don't you have some place to be?"

"To be or not to be . . . high . . . that is the question."

"You ought to get stoned on your own time."

"Time belongs to all humanity."

"Are you always this obnoxious?"

"The walls are closing in and you're still spinning shit to swine."

"I think you should go."

"If this is reality, then there can be nothing but madness!"

He strutted off down the hall singing "Paint It Black" at the top of his lungs.

I went back to *Crime and Punishment*, but I was unsettled.

I knew what I would do. I would call his stepfather. It was later that I understood why I did that. I didn't want to get him in trouble; I wanted him to take my class.

I wanted to know him.

I wanted to change him.

His stepfather responded as predictably as I knew he would. I talked about the need for bright kids to be in a qualitatively different environment. He loved the idea of disciplined guided reading of the classics. And did I insist they write with Cartesian logic? I assured him of a rigidity a military academy would admire. He assured me "the situation will be rectified first thing Monday morning." My hand was icicle-cold as I put down the receiver.

"You Machiavellian manipulator, I hope you know you'll regret this ploy."

From the tone of Dubie's voice, I was ready to believe him.

"Where the fuck do we sit in this place?"

"On your ass."

He sat down in the front row, put his backpack on the desk, his feet on top of the backpack, and folded his arms.

The other kids hated him immediately. He relished their animosity.

"Why did Raskolnikov kill the lady for intellectual reasons?"

"He was a weird dude."

"He'd lost his faith in Christ."

"He was poor and had to take it out on somebody."

Dubie Wexler rolled his eyes in exaggerated patience. "You guys are mediocre stupidity personified."

They reacted to his tone with hostile groans.

"Perhaps you'd like to enlighten us, Mr. Wexler."

"Exceptionals always kill commons. And then they get high to forget."

A straight-A student told him he was elitist and his allusions to drugs were juvenile. I secretly admired her at that moment.

"Freedom for adolescents is a shower for a Jew."

Bonnie Rabinowitz told him he was disgusting. That failed to move him.

"Discipline is our reward for self-freedom."

"This discussion is getting us nowhere," I offered, trying to control the quickly escalating anger level, including my own.

"It's all nowhere. It's just a question of degree." Dubie sighed and looked down.

We went on with class. I was quite pleased with my leadership ability until I realized he was asleep.

I woke him up after class. He came to, slowly scanning the room for enemies. There were none, save me.

"You got any uppers?"

"No, I don't."

"Know where I can score some speed?"

"What do you think?"

"I think I'm sick of this horseshit already."

"You know, Dubie Wexler, you do have a brain in that chemical factory of a head."

"I like your clothes."

I wasn't ready for that. Most of my students shriek at my ideas of fashion, which they see as Early Goodwill Unmatched Frenzy.

"Thank you."

He was shuffling in his backpack. A copy of *Mein Kampf* fell out onto the floor. I picked it up for him. He didn't thank me. He lit up a joint.

"For Christ's sake, Dubie, put that out! Do you want to get busted?"

"I want to get high."

"You'll get me fired."

"Ah, the threat of economic insecurity. Works wonders on the best of them."

"Put it out!"

"Do you like weapons?"

"Not especially."

"I do. Guns fascinate me."

"What do I have to do to get you to oust that joint?"

"Have a hit."

I grabbed it from him with a sly smile and stomped it out on the floor.

"Cunt."

"Don't talk like that to me."

"You're like all the rest. Scratch the surface and she's a bourgeois sellout."

I completely lost my temper. "Listen, you little arrogant shit, I was in SDS when you were toilet training, picketing People's Park when you were playing on the jungle gym, and bailing people out of jail while you scored your first joint from some rich little self-indulgent pisshead and got cosmic in a one-hundred-thousand-dollar home."

I was yelling by now. When I'm really mad, I usually get silent. He smiled a stoner's grin and rattled his curls.

"I knew it. I just knew it."

He walked out the door crooning. "She talks just like a woman."

I cried when he left.

He badgered and goaded me all semester. I'd find notes scrawled in manic handwriting stuffed in my purse, wedged in my lesson plans, written on the napkin in my lunchbag. These fiery epistles included the Hell's Angels Code of Violence, Hunter Thompson's treatise on acid tripping, Dubie's death poetry replete with violent metaphor and macabre imagery.

He was stoned every day.

Sometimes he'd be so weird that I was scared for him.

"Space is warped by matter. Therefore minds are warped by knowledge."

"Why is everything so bleak for you, Dubie?"

"Is this Psychology One?"

"Have you ever considered therapy?"

"For what?"

"Help to function, for one."

"LSD consumes forty-seven percent of its weight in excess reality."

"That's escapism."

"I get stoned to enhance my life."

"Balls."

"Let's get stoned together and talk about Hitler."

"What?"

"I want to know if Hitler was a reflection of society or is society a reflection of Adolf Hitler?"

I was tired that afternoon, not up to obsessive rhetorical questions.

"Why do you want to talk about Hitler?"

"In the not-too-distant future, all but a chosen few will die in the holocaust."

"What did you take, Dubie?"

"I took your fucking course."

"What *drug* did you take at lunch?"

"I didn't."

"That's a lie."

"The Sex Pistols are actually the Osmonds on peyote."

"That's not funny."

"Life is a box that leaks around the edges."

"Tell me what you're on!"

"I tried to kill myself with paraquat, but I kept on getting stoned."

"I'm not amused, Dubie."

"Do you love your husband?"

"Yes. Very much."

"Why did you get married?"

"It was easier than living together."

"Does he love you?"

"I hope so."

"I can tell when you guys are fighting."

He named dates and incidents in class. He was deadly accurate.

"Dubie, let me take you home."

He gave me a tour through his house. No one was home. He showed me the dinner table where he was forced into family dinners; the utterly tasteless living room in which I recognized certain images in his poetry—the blue curtains, the sad sofa with wilted flowers, the pseudo early-American furniture littered with church bulletins and Fuller Brush pamphlets. There were mountains of Budweiser cans in the kitchen.

His room was ordered and spotless. Led Zeppelin, Che Guevara, and Bob Dylan were lined up in perfect symmetry. Copies of leftist newspapers were neatly stacked in the bottom of his closet, where two pairs of Adidas stood side by side. His books were meticulously organized in alphabetical order, from Amin to the Zodiac killer. There were no curtains or bedspread. He tucked his sheets with hospital corners.

He fell back onto his bed and went to sleep.

I left.

He was stoned again the next day.

I got mad and threw him out.

I insulted him in front of the class.

I felt guilty.

He came after school and we laughed. I whispered to him, "Well, at least we know the point where we'd make up and go to bed if this were real life."

"I don't want to hurt you. I just want to learn to cry."

"Then stop taking drugs."

"Maybe."

An enraged YMCA volunteer handed me a piece of paper one day.

"This was copied from the men's room. I know it's Wexler's and he's disgusting."

"Why give it to me?"

"Because you're the only one who can stand his barbiturate rages."

"And?"

"Why don't you kick him out?"

I had no answer.

At the Urinal

Iron clad
In the mad
of ad and fad,
I unzip
Silly billy unswaddled
crotch
Varoom!
A wilted parsnip
Undisciplined heirloom
In the fingertip grip
Of the fellowship
of drip.

I assured him Dubie meant no harm. I still choose to believe that.

He's off in college. I don't know if he's off drugs. I like to believe I had a sensible influence on him and that he gave them up. God knows I campaigned enough. I wanted to be significant to him.

It was tough saying good-bye to Dubie.

He wrote me a note on my pay voucher.

> M + M is a sweet flower
> Most love her looks
> Few can smell her
> You come as close as anyone Dube.

The bank cashed it anyway.

Portrait of the Artist as a Young Woman

In Southern California one becomes a semanticist, a linguist, and a translator by force of circumstance.

Bad means good, far out means righteous, which means to the max, so you can go for it and be blown away or ozoned out because it's cash.

One gets immune to talk of redemption in yeast, Nirvana, or Satori; Jesus as a cosmic light; meditation as a cure for manic depression; soybean salvation; megavitamins; yoga; Rolfing; or reexperiencing one's birth trauma in a redwood hot tub.

That is why I should not even have reacted when I first interviewed Tamara for a place in the Advanced Writing Seminar. I thought I was being polite, not philosophical.

"Hello, Tamara. How are you?"

"Where I am is where I want to be."

I shouldn't have been surprised. These fragments of conversation transpire daily. I know at least six kids' mantras; I can time some of them as they lapse into the nothingness of inner peace.

I have heard the sermons regarding the benefits to the lymphatic system of fasting and watermelon purges.

I know about Krishnamurti, Guru Maharaj-ji, Yogananda, the Tibetan lamas, and the Ascended Masters. I have been lectured to by various students on the advantages of being celestially sealed in marriage, divinely enlightened on earth, and flowing with the ebb of the universe somewhere in between.

"Tamara, why do you want this particular class?"

"Why does a person want anything? To grow."

"Fair enough. Are you college bound?"

"Why are you asking me all these questions?"

"There is limited space in the class."

"Space can't be limited."

"Tamara, do you want or need this class?"

"Yes. I paint all the time and need to write more."

I knew she was an artist, because the Art Department discussed her so often. She was something of a rarity in their domain. She didn't recreate album covers or watercolor the perfect wave. She didn't throw earthtone pots or mold extraterrestrial creatures for the kiln. She did not batik pillow covers in surrealistic tones or weave hemplike hymns to wall decorating.

She painted. In oils. Large canvases of vibrant color and depth-charged imagination. I had seen some of her tableaux. She was a whimsical Munch drowning in a rainbow of sweet morbidity. Featureless heads careened like helium balloons at sunset while immobile mouths and eyes waited silently in the corners.

"Closest thing I've had to a painter yet," was the summation of Barnett, the art teacher, and the closest thing to a compliment that I can recall him saying about anyone.

I let her into the class.

Her papers were spacy, semispiritual bouquets of rambling run-on sentences and free-child fragments.

It is hard to build a case in defense of academic structure when dealing with children of enlightened parents. First of all, you are regarded as a member of the "not yet there" category of antiquated pedagogues. Secondly, there is an unceasing demand to explain the why of structure, when evidence points to man's infinite capacity to communicate amid seeming chaos. And lastly, the do-as-I-say-because-I-am-the-teacher flat out doesn't work. These children do not accept dominance/submission as a tenet of human interaction. They see that as psychically restrictive and spiritually damaging. These children operate from the privileged position of I-rule-my-own-space.

I still put F's on her papers. Her arguments made no sense, followed no visible line of reasoning, and yet she defended her metaphysical meanderings with a crushing finality.

"You just don't see where I'm coming from."

"That's the whole point; it's not made clear."

"I can't write when you tell me how."

"Tamara, I'm not saying I believe in this format as the

only means of self-expression. But this is not creative writing."

"All writing is creative, since it stems from the self."

"Are you going to college?"

She tossed her shoulder-length, chestnut-brown hair and nodded affirmatively. She was beautiful in an exotic manner, a softer version of Rita Moreno with overtones of Rita Tushingham.

"Then you have to learn to write an introduction, a body, and a conclusion."

"But why?"

The temptation to yelp "Because I say so!" is always only epidermally away in these situations, but closely governed and rehearsed behavior has taught me other avenues of expression.

"Tamara, if you choose to rusticate yourself on some remote pig farm and write stratospheric prose, fine. But if you're going to Berkeley as you say you are, you will flunk out with papers like these."

"But why?"

"Because you have said nothing in a rather grandiose fashion."

"Dr. Froth thought my papers were advanced thinking."

The mention of the man who billed himself as author, comic, consultant, scientist, magician, and new-age physicist made my stomach acid drip. Beach communities seem to be meccas for self-styled gurus with credentials earned from matchbook covers; they come and create "schools" attractive to progressive parents whose flock of below-grade-level kids have not had their inner wonderfulness tapped by traditional education. For fees that rival Stanford University's, these children reach, grow, flower, bloom, expand, become, and self-actualize in richly controlled environments where neophyte narcissism conceals absence of ability.

Tamara had been an apostle of Froth's Free Thinking and Attention Institute. Her junior high curriculum was composed of Birds and Flowers (seventh grade), Fruits and Rocks (eighth grade), Space Time and Galaxy (ninth grade). Her transcript included Dr. Froth's philosophy of education alongside the course description. "I want to share how outrageous the universe can really be. Think of the wonder, the mystery, the marvel of it all. Life is cosmic."

Tamara's parents were jazz musicians, quite well known in their field. They were the sort of people who would never appear at a Back-to-School Night, so my only glimpse of them was at a dive near Oceanside, where they were jamming with a few friends.

They were talented musicians. Mother played the saxophone and scat sang. Dad worked the piano and drums. The rest of the ensemble was composed of social nudist friends of theirs. The whole group made jewelry by day under the label of Life Theater, Inc. Recent financial setbacks due to her mother's health forced Tamara to go to public high school. Her teachers puzzled her; Dr. Froth's staff were trained to be free floaters in the mystifying world of relativity and the quantum. Apparently we were not.

"I still don't see the point of a premise."

"You have to make yourself clear to argue your point with persuasion."

"But I'm not persuading; I'm just being on paper."

"Your beingness is still poorly written."

"I think you're being unreceptive and only judging from one external level."

I wanted to rage on about the superficiality of that kind of semantic exchange, but instead I just plagiarized Joan Didion's doggerel about writing.

"I am still committed to the idea that the ability to think for oneself depends on one's mastery of the language."

"Well, I'm not so sure. We intuit most of the world. I don't think about form when I paint."

"But you're painting for yourself, right?"

That lovely waterfall of brown rippled down another yes.

"Here you have to explain things back to someone else."

"Maybe we're all not on the same trip."

She'd rejected what I said.

I had assigned the reading of a book to my class to show them how to write a formal review. I consciously forbade *The Hobbit, Teachings of Don Juan, Watership Down, Jonathan Livingston Seagull,* and Linda Goodman's *Sun Signs.*

I requested that they consider a classic novel as a source of new enrichment. Two chose *Anna Karenina,* three picked

The Red and the Black, a few selected *The Idiot,* while some of the diehards stuck with Hemingway.

Tamara had a liberated libido fit.

"*Journey to Ixtlan* is my choice and you've put limits on my freedom!"

I think I said "Bingo."

"But you can't do that!"

"I just did, Tamara. Read that on your own. How about some Flaubert?"

"Is that like Rose Hips?"

"No. He's an author from the nineteenth century."

"What about Adelle Davis?"

"She's not a fiction writer."

"What's that got to do with anything?"

"Would you like some suggestions on an author?"

"I'm gonna go paint." She flipped her mahogany mane back in a defiant arabesque and trotted her Birkenstock sandals out the door.

I didn't see her again for two weeks. When she came back, I scarcely recognized her. She had taken scissors and hacked at her hair. Tresses of different jagged contours hugged the round crown of her scalp. The coiffure corresponded to the disquietude of her eyes.

"Do I have to stay here today? I want to paint."

I let her go.

She came back a week later with a form for dropping out of school. I assumed some monetary windfall had avalanched a transfer to another free school. I remember feeling slightly hostile as I checked in her materials and tried to come up with a grade at time of leaving.

Her seaweed-green eyes took inventory around the room as if she were identifying each piece of furniture as "my table," "my file cabinet," "my bookcase," "my teacher."

"My mother is dying."

I did not know what to say.

"I want to be with her when she dies."

I said I understood. That she had made a wise and compassionate decision. She looked like a wounded Joan of Arc; her painter's fingers trembled.

"Will you keep in touch, Tamara?"

"Barnett said I could still come and paint."

"Good."

I meant that on several levels, but didn't know how to tell her. She didn't say good-bye to me.

Barnett said I could see her paintings if I was really interested.

I was, but my interests were different from his.

The canvases were impressive frescoes of airborne madonnas floating over Goyaesque figures struggling on the ground. The shrouded virgins had horizontal heads with vertical eyes painted sunburst yellow. Their arms were folded, ready to receive an infant, but they were empty. In the vacant spaces, she had painted gray holes, the color of rhinoceros skin, that looked like flat gun-metal funnels leading nowhere.

Barnett hovered behind me, reeking of turpentine.

"She's a helluvan artist. No pretense in her stroke. Helluva painter."

I wanted to sock him.

She came to see me one day when I was being observed by the administration for my yearly evaluation. The evaluation form itself contained two grammatical errors and a misplaced modifier. My evaluator was an ex-industrial arts teacher cum football coach from the Coachella Valley who had previously confided in me that "academics aren't where it's at for kids." He listened politely, but I knew he was bored and I was nervous. He would write some inane comment about good eye contact, we both would sign it, and it would be stashed away in my file. The process is repeated every year.

He noticed Tamara. He made a note of her intrusion on his clipboard. She had Yonnido, her German shepherd, with her. He noted that also. Animals and nonstudents, both illegal on campus and subject to prosecution.

I tried to ignore all of them and get on with Thackeray. I did a lousy job at both. Yonnido barked at a girl with pompoms on her Nikes, Tamara tried to hush her and felled the desk in the process, which hit Mr. Ramirez on the tops of his white Florsheims.

The class went downhill from there.

Tamara remained silent and standing throughout the fracas. Her gaunt frame frosted with the uneven crown of thorns looked eerily like the Angels of Auschwitz kids saw in history books.

She waited until the room was empty and quiet. I had never noticed how her thick eyebrows formed an unruly line across her forehead.

"My mother is dying. I do not have another."

I said I was sorry.

"Her eyes can't close because she's too tired to shut them."

I listened and watched her pace.

"She talks to me about being a woman and then they give her the shots and she doesn't make sense."

I nodded that I understood. Her eyes squeezed down to angry slits that choked out tears.

"Dr. Froth says cancer is caused by anger and that pent-up hostility makes cancer spread."

"Dr. Froth is full of shit, Tamara."

"He said that serious researchers proved that your bad feelings give you cancer."

"Do you believe that, Tamara?"

"I can't believe my mother who plays the saxophone is mad enough to want to die."

"I can't either."

"But Dr. Froth said . . ."

"Fuck Dr. Froth and his holistic theories."

"She only weighs eighty pounds," Tamara went on disconsolately. She looked like a muddled angel in a foxhole. "The bones in her hands stick out like dead branches."

"Is she in the hospital now?"

She signaled a resigned yes.

She let me hug her for an instant, all tangled up like stiff foliage. She had scratched her scalp raw. She didn't cry.

"Will you come again, Tamara?"

"If you can talk yourself well, you can think yourself sick." She hissed that out as a conclusion. She broke loose and fled.

I saw her three weeks later. Barnett had told me that her mother had died.

Tamara looked relieved and tired. She stood outside my door with Yonnido after school. I asked her to come in, but she requested that we stay in the sun. It was March and cloudy.

"I'm sorry to hear about your mother." Hollow, hollow words of sympathy resounding in a corridor.

"My mother is dead."

"I'm so sorry."

"They were very rough with her body when they wrapped it afterwards. I told them to be more gentle."

She had been with her when she died. The image of a shrouded saxophone player serpented its way into my dream calendar.

"What will you do now?"

"My dad and I are going to Esalen for a week, then I'm coming back to school."

I wanted to know which school, but I didn't ask.

She reregistered two weeks later—for four art classes, Biology, and an elective called Self-discovery, taught by a man who wore jumpsuits, lived in a dome, and studied silence with large groups of meditators.

Everyone marveled at her recovery. She won two awards for her oil paintings. She went on a fast, rekindled her interest in surfing, and let her hair grow to her collarbone.

Her dad gave her a lei of bright red carnations for her graduation robe. I watched him during the ceremony, his angular face frozen in a collage of loss. Dr. Froth was with him.

I took her robe and handed her a diploma in return.

"Let me hear from you, Tamara. Keep in touch." Those hesitant flamethrower eyes seemed surprised that I asked.

She did not keep in touch but I have been informed that she went to Europe with the new jazz ensemble and lapsed into uncontrolled bulimia. Her skeletal frame blossomed into obesity. She has been hospitalized four times for aggressive depression. Her father had remarried. Dr. Froth is importing ginseng and running the Carling Nutrition Co-op in a nearby beach town.

The local art show at the county fair produced an odd assortment of winners this year. Second place went to an embossed road map of Borrego. Stuffed stocking statuary claimed honorable mentions. A still life of a papaya took the sweepstakes. At the eastern end of Bing Crosby Hall, just left of the fire extinguisher, I spied her entry.

The colors were so familiar, but the whimsy of surrealism was supplanted by a primitive anatomical realism. Tamara had drawn an aerial skeleton with a hydrocephalic head. The skull was painted as poster art of an ersatz phrenologist. A rainbow of violent colors labeled the emotions—purple for anger, red for rage, green for jealousy, brown for self-destruction, yellow for loneliness. The emaciated starveling ascended toward a cheerless labyrinth of black sky, where cell-like explosions starred up the galaxy.

Just below the metatarsal bone, a tiny tin saxophone hung like a limp pelican chirping melancholy notes to the watermelon in the corner.

Karmic Pole-vaulting in the Ionosphere

The painful truth of my entire existence is that I've never been "with it." Not that efforts weren't made.

In the seventh grade, I paid Lydia Gomez ten dollars to make me a sack dress from the tablecloth I had ripped off from O Sol O Mia's Pizzeria. I wore it with fake flowers at the neck, never noticing that cinch belts and sweaters were the craze.

I used the word *cherry* for years, thinking it meant "red car."

I painted Twiggy lines on my eyes when the natural look cleaned up America. I have never heard a Peter Frampton record.

I hate Perrier water.

I sleep in socks.

Marijuana makes me tired and cranky. I still mistake a

roach clip for one of those blackhead removers you send away for to *Ingenue* magazine. I bought a scarf ring at Bullock's two years ago, but I am yet unable to muster enough fashion fluency to learn to use it.

I did not know who O. J. was in the Hertz commercial.

I used "get down" as a reasonable command until a student finally informed me that "let's screw" was its current synonym.

I have never seen one episode of *Charlie's Angels, Happy Days,* or *Laverne and Shirley.*

Health food gives me hives.

In short, I have been relegated by some genetic discrepancy to be a sideliner at the pop culture festival.

I confess to a certain vicarious appreciation of varying degrees of hipness. Certain out-of-focus trendsetters pique my imagination and solicit my envious applause in the soundproof booths of my soul.

That's why I noticed Cloud.

It wasn't her use of almond extract as natural scent or the tinkling of various bells from selected loops or even her fanciful appellation, Rainbow Cloud Kamali, that captured my imagination. It was her nails, all ten of them. Starting from her thumb on her left hand, there were depicted a ranunculus, an iris, a daisy, an azalea, and a poppy. Her right hand was no less bountiful: a geranium, a violet, a lily of the valley, an orchid, and one lone white rose. Each finger had been meticulously groomed and orchestrated to represent the proper flower with the proper colors. Tiny stamens veined their way toward her cuticles. An occasional leaf sidewinded along the curve. Miniature masterpieces of botanical splendor.

Sometimes her eyelids were black and white chessboards, carefully framing her downsloped, lidded eyes. Her ears were pierced in three places.

She wore ankle bracelets made from ornamental seeds.

She drew tattoos on her shoulder. During the fall semester, I kept track. There was a penciled Streisand profile, Bob Dylan's hat from *The Last Waltz* (that was explained to me by a high and verbal rock groupie who saw Cloud as replacing Patti Smith), a hookah complete with nacreous-looking smoke crawling toward her clavicle, and a faint replica of Spielberg's space ship from *Close Encounters.*

I loved Mondays, when I could look forward to what Cloud had conjured up over the weekend. She went through an occult period where all art forms were black, including the polish on her nails.

I took her nonparticipation in class as part of her aversion to convention. She never took part in any discussions. She'd check out her books, read them promptly, and turn them in within a week with a written evaluation on homemade stationery.

Most of the books bored her, but Holden Caulfield found an ally in Cloud. Instead of a review, she wrote him a love letter of effusive praise. According to Cloud, "Holden had his shit together where it counted and set the goddamn phonies of the world on a hide 'n' seek for more far out unions like his and Phoebe's."

That particular semester a group of fundamentalist Christians had rampaged through the heathen subjects of fiction and zeroed in on my class as the ultimate example of moral decay. I was denounced as an atheistic polluter of young minds, distributing vile trash like *The Catcher in the Rye* in a godless atmosphere supported by tax dollars.

Several parents requested I select another book for their children. Most of the kids thought the book was interesting, although some thought Holden was "a self-centered geek who'd probably play water polo if he went to a regular school."

Cloud thought Holden was a prophet who would "catch all the kids who fall then move to Britain and be friends with David Bowie." She fantasized that Holden would have "unceasing wealth, a fur-lined Bentley with a private telephone, a clean penthouse on the Thames, and velvet blazers the color of Johnny Rotten's shoes."

This was one of the rare writings composed during her black period, so I let her allusions elude me and told her I was impressed with her admiration for Holden. I remember that day because Cloud had woven her hair in a series of plaits, which swayed like dancing kelp beds when she walked. Each braid was fastened with a rubber band and a minuscule bell like the ones Hare Krishna women wear on their sashes. She tinkled a mini ice-cream truck symphony each time she moved.

She was reading a witchcraft manual while the rest read Paul Zindel. I rang a tress.

She jingled in my direction.

"I liked your letter to Holden. He's one of my favorites too."

She smiled ever so slightly so as not to distort the four-leaf clover she'd drawn on her chin.

Her eyes were two shocking shiners, a perfect mélange of black and blue. I assumed it was the punk motif and decided she'd leaned a bit too much toward the charcoal.

She chimed back to her corner with a breezy "Thanks."

The counselor came to see me after school. A nice man who places kids in classes where they can "relate." I'm not sure what the yardstick is, but I generally liked his selections in matchmaking. He'd placed Cloud in my class because our first names were unusual. I have been told that he put a kid in a Physical Science class because his hobby was building warships. The science teacher spends his time watching *Victory at Sea* reruns. Apparently that union failed.

"Mrs. Kamali would like to see you about Cloud."

"Sure. Tell her to book an appointment."

"She's in my office." He sighed.

"Sounds like she's occupied it."

"Well, she's not leaving until she sees you, is the closest I came to decoding her rantings."

"Is it *The Catcher in the Rye* again?"

"I'll tell her you'll be right down."

My plans for an afternoon of clandestine chocolate-eating and junk-novel reading were fading.

Most parent conferences transpire rather uneventfully, except for the God-squad fanatics, whose gusto is slightly frightening.

Those who vigil at school can usually be divided into four categories: the denial diehards, the defense leaguers, the vicarious vipers, or the discipline disciples. In any event, most instructors leave these confabs with another insight into the student. Usually compassion, or uncomfortable assumptions about genetics.

I was not prepared for Mrs. Kamali. She lunged at me before I was inside the office. She looked like an abused version of an overweight Shelley Winters. She wore a black matte jersey top over stoplight-red stretch pants. She was braless, shoeless, and seemingly fearless. Her eyes switched gears every five seconds.

Two hamhock hands squeezed my shoulder blades. Her breath was hot and smelled of stale cigarettes.

"My daughter loves you, but she *hates* your class."

I tried to breathe like a Lamaze lady trying to relax.

"I'm gonna tell you a few things about Cloud, okay?"

I would have agreed to anything if she would only release her grip.

"I'll just sit here, Mrs. Kamali." She let me go. I scooted across the room and sat in the desk chair. I pulled out the sliding slab used for typewriters and plunked my purse between us.

She dragged her chair closer.

"You don't understand my Rainbow Cloud, see what I mean?"

"Well, perhaps you can detail the problem for me."

"My Cloud is a night people like I am and she bends spoons with her mind."

"I see!" I said, not seeing.

"My Cloud and me are real smart types with high IQs but we clash because of our former lives."

I nodded to her that I understood, which I did not.

"See, in our other lives she was an abbess and I was a rebel monk, so she killed me. I knew it soon as she was born. She fought me off in her crib."

"Yes, that could be a problem."

"Well, I'm fire sign and she's water, so that should tell you something. Anyway her vibes about me are so bad she distorts the TV when she walks by."

She leaned forward and put her hands on my purse. I wondered if anyone was left in the counseling office.

"We didn't always live like this, you know. They made me move back to where there was a school."

I knew that Cloud had been a transfer student, but nothing about her background.

"We had a good life in the hills. Me, Cloud, Oceana, that's her sister, and my old man. It was primo being without electricity and water. Our periods were synchronized just like the hogs."

"Why did you leave."

"They made us. Girls have to be in school. Hell, I had books and we all got into Primals."

"Mrs. Kamali, what do you see as the problem?"

"Cloud and me we fight. She tells me that she'll throw a spell my way with me tied to the railroad tracks, but I didn't hit her."

"You're having problems with your daughter?"

"Those black eyes are bad karma. I tell her negative energy makes your skin bad, but she don't listen."

"Those black eyes were real?"

"In a spiritual sense, yes. Pisces are self-destructive."

"Did you get into a fight?"

"She'll never do your papers cuz she don't want anyone to know her except me."

It occurred to me that indeed Cloud would not turn in regular assignments like opinion essays.

"Her eyes made two holes in my bedroom door. She knows I don't have it good with my old man."

I nodded and watched her squeeze my bag until her knuckles were white.

"You know I made it through the westward movement. She knows that and she's jealous."

By now I was intrigued and only slightly frightened.

"We stay up all night and write things, but you won't get to see 'em. She played a symphony on the glasses without touching them."

I shifted positions; she thought I was getting up, so she reached out to shove me back. She got me square in the sternum.

"Cloud wrote me a letter in invisible ink. I didn't like it."

"What did it say?"

"That she was gonna be the rock 'n' roll governor of California stationed in Catalina in a huge mansion that's all tidy and neat, but I don't get to come."

"That sounds angry." I felt the need to hear my own voice. She looked like a sad walrus sitting there.

"Cloud don't like me in the day. We only communicate at night."

"Do you stay up late together?"

"You mean she never told you? She sleeps after school and gets up at midnight. We spook around until dawn. By the way, she hates your books too."

She rose. Her pendulous breasts bounced off the waistband of her pants.

She gave me a broad grin, a gentle shove, and some advice.

"Don't ever put her up in front of the class, because she can explode your carburetor by moving her thumbs. Like this."

She wiggled her thumbs in a frantic Fonzie and waddled out.

I searched for a colleague to talk to. No one.

I jogged to my car, conscious of the carburetor, although I have never seen one and its precise location in a Volkswagen is still a mystery.

I started to observe if Cloud looked tired. She had entered her Harlequin period, so it was hard to tell. Tiny charcoaled teardrops melted down her rouged cheeks. Smiles were painted on her nails, happy smiles, semismiles, vicious smiles. Her tattoos became mini-rodents with curled tails. She was reading a paperback called *Poltergeist Patter* while the rest of the class trekked through *The Treasure of the*

Sierra Madre. Almond extract changed to the pungent odor of musk. She tied bows of yarn around her ankles and wrists.

We never talked about her mother. However, on three occasions I ran into Mrs. Kamali. Once she was wandering around campus in a kaleidoscope caftan, talking to no one in particular. I said hello, but she did not recognize me.

The second time was at the fish counter of Safeway during an unexpected rainy spell. I saw her loitering near the scallops. Her hair was sopping wet and dripped a puddle on the floor. She edged over to the shrimp section and nudged me in the ribs.

"My Cloud speaks Kalmuck. She spied these shellfish in the Ionian Sea and transmigrated 'em during *Johnny Carson.*"

I thanked her and checked out in the express lane.

I was asked to be a speaker at a Gifted Parents Association meeting held in a local church. The entire concept of the organization unnerves me; however, my principal gave me an unambivalent message about attending. To my horror, it was a full house. Row upon row of anxious faces of Mensa mothers sitting primly in polyester pantsuits next to the younger radical-chic parents, who sported jeans and T-shirts with sayings like HAVE YOU HUGGED YOUR KID TODAY? or CHILDREN ARE PEOPLE TOO neatly printed on the front.

I don't know what I said to them, but they laughed. The other two speakers gave serious talks on the importance of creative playthings.

During the question-and-answer period she stood up, out of nowhere.

Her wild hair took off in all directions. She was laden with Egyptian jewelry hanging on her Mexican wedding dress.

"You've been avoiding me," she shrieked from the next to the last row. Her finger was pointing at me.

At least I didn't faint. The audience sat in stunned silence. Mrs. Kamali didn't notice.

"You don't know nothing from gifts here. Games don't mean moving the couch with your mind."

The president of the organization stood up and thanked her for her contribution and suggested they move on to the business part of the meeting. She thanked us for our valued input.

We were excused.

I slouched out of the sanctuary, hoping Mrs. Kamali wouldn't follow me.

Her jewelry clanged behind me.

"I don't like these groups," she whispered into the night.

"I don't either."

Mutuality at last.

"My Cloud asked me to come and hear you talk."

I thanked her and headed toward my car. She got inside a beat-up truck. I caught her silhouette in the rearview mirror. Cloud had been waiting for her. I traced the outline of her three-ponytail pyramid hairdo in the reflection of the car lights.

We never talked about it.

In the spring Cloud underwent a regressive metamorphosis and became a mock Shirley Temple. She corkscrew-curled her hair, wore collars made of doilies, ruffled skirts, and Mary Janes. Instead of *The Heart Is a Lonely Hunter,* she read Nancy Drew mysteries with Enankar pamphlets as bookmarks.

We had a last-day-of-school party.

Cloud gave me a blank Mother's Day card with an original poem about a dragon with slobbering jaws and jagged claws who eats little Rollo and subsequently needs a Tums.

She wrote a note on the back:

> May the hippopotamus of happiness eat the water weeds of war out of your pool of life.

She signed it by sketching an enormous cloud in the distinct shape of Catalina. There was a star marked Avalon, with musical notes tooting upward from her Governor's Mansion.

Californians refer to Jerry Brown as the Zen politician with the rock-star girl friend.

Jarvis/Gann passed by a landslide.

Perhaps there's a place for Cloud in government after all. You never know the effects of sunstroke on the public. I like to contemplate her campaign strategy. She'd probably get my vote.

Read 'em and Weep

Special Education is one of those bureaucratic umbrellalike labels that allow for huge amounts of tax dollars to be held in reserve and doled out according to whatever is the pet project in current vogue. The need for special classes is undeniable, and with the raising of public consciousness, special programs have been instituted for children classified as educationally handicapped, educably mentally retarded, aphasiac, visually handicapped, and culturally disadvantaged.

The problem lies in identification and definition. Who belongs where?

There are kids with problems and there are problem kids. The division is not always clear. For decades, bilingual kids whose lives straddle two cultures have been labeled slow while their Anglo counterparts who have no problem responding to an equation in English have been called gifted.

In the more recent past, kids with severe disabilities have

been turned away. Parents have been left to their own resources to find facilities that meet their special requirements.

No longer.

The Handicapped Children's Act Search and Serve Program obligates each school district to create a special learning environment for children with unique needs.

I cheer for the long overdue legislation, but I contemplate its implementation with great trepidation.

The age of humanistic "let's bake Indian bread instead of reading" approach has been supplanted by a back-to-basics reverence for the automated age. Computers, calculators, videotape recorders, data processors, and talk-back television sets are the new Technoriculum.

I remain marginally unimpressed.

Parents sigh as SAT scores decline. *Newsweek* devotes a cover story to why Johnny can't read. The family blames the school, teachers blame the family, the churches indict all of us, linguistic experts tell us times are changing, local governments get antsy, school boards take a hard line and allocate money for a task force of leisure-suited experts to rectify the situation.

Such was the cycle of revamping the reading program in California a few years ago. Sacramento was placing a heavy hand on basic skills. Each district had to submit post-test proofs of improvement.

Technocracy was summoned to the rescue. Educational Development Labs sprang up like unwanted relatives. Each offered a complete "system" for overhauling remedial reading programs, complete with demonstrations of the latest machines disguised as in-service training.

We were ordered to attend, to learn the lab approach to a total reading system. Our corporate guru was John Flansbaum of Teaching Communications Technology, Inc. He had the most annoying, sinusy whine I've heard since a NyQuil commercial. He explained each machine from history of conception to the final paint job. The idea was to equip a classroom with centers geared for each separate skill. The cost per room was around forty thousand dollars. The price included six tape decks on which a story was initially played; six guided readers, for reading the story by a light that traced the sentences; six viewmates, to flash the significant vocabulary at ten-second intervals; six workbooks, to check the same vocabulary, called *Searching Out the Words*; and one tachistoscope, whose function and pronunciation were both suspect. Mr. Flansbaum explained with blocked olfactory fervor the statistical rates of success in districts in Nebraska, the grade-level jumps in Albuquerque.

Most of my colleagues tuned him out after the first utterance of the word *concept*, which he employed approximately three hundred times in two hours.

We were less than enthusiastic until the first day of school, when we were rendered nearly hysterical by one sentence spoken as an aside by a counselor: "Your reading labs will be filled with the Special Education kids, so you'll want to pay a bit more attention to the equipment."

The rough translation of this pronouncement is as follows:

none of us was qualified to teach Special Education; none of us had much sympathy with machinery; all of us knew certain educationally handicapped kids liked to break things; forty thousand dollars means you're accountable, period.

We hid our terror from each other in an effort not to appear prejudiced or closed-minded.

I did not understand the machines.

I was nervous about being responsible for them and resented being told to use them.

The kids went crazy.

"Far fuckin' out; pinball machines!"

"Did you bring your Kiss tapes?"

"This light goes up to a thousand words a minute."

"You got no movies in Spanish?"

By the second week of school, I had made three conclusive discoveries:

1. Absolutely no one listened to the story tapes at all; they brought their own.
2. The film for the vocabulary viewmate had been sufficiently tampered with so "fuck you" blinked at ten-second intervals in two different languages, with an occasional reference to the same act about a member of your family.
3. The guided readers had been perfectly adjusted to trace the graffiti on the wall at exactly 347 words per minute.

The room was chaos. The Chicanos had invaded the Listening Center, kicking out the Bee Gees fanatics in favor of a group called Guapo. The hyperactive kids from the Educationally Handicapped classes spent their time inserting pencils into the tachistoscope as the arm of the machine fell, flashing a series of numbers in less than a second for eye-training exercises. The dyslexic children stuck to the vocabulary machines, where they made paying games out of their guesses. Three of the retarded kids sat placidly in a quiet reading area and thumbed through encyclopedias. The workbooks were out of order by the second day, and the vocabulary tapes had been put in backwards so many times that the sprocket holes were now caverns. Several kids who were supposedly on medication for hyperactivity neglected to take it sometimes and would grab the nearest object, usually a hardback dictionary, and bash their neighbor in the head.

I was supposed to be keeping individual records on each kid. I could barely maintain order. I settled fights those first few weeks, tried to subdue my flagrant paranoia about the kids breaking the machines I hated in the first place. I did not know their names; there was no time to get acquainted. From bell to bell I braced myself for the belch and fart of automated information churning prefabricated vignettes on *What My Flag Means to Me* in measured beams on segmented burps of vocabulary. The checkup tests at the end of the sequences were objects of the absurd. If taken at all, they were raced through for speed without a glance at the question. Most were checked under the tables, stuffed in motors, or sailed across the room as rudimentary aircraft. I learned the depth and breadth of meaning in the word *hyperkinetic.*

In response to frequent frustration tears, my boss told me to "wing it." The kids told me to "shine it," and Mr. Flansbaum told me to reread my manuals.

After two months of minimal functioning at maximum tension, I became aware of having committed an almost clichéd infraction of education.

I had neglected to notice the quiet kid, the one who causes no problem.

It occurred to me as I was separating two boys who were fencing with the guided readers. I pried them apart and focused on the one sitting Indian-style in front of the closed-circuit videotape recorder. I had unhooked it three days ago after a dismal attempt by the thespians to do a takeoff on *The Gong Show.* When I wasn't standing guard, kids would plug it in to the school cable and watch cartoons. This boy just sat there staring at the blank screen.

I screamed at a girl who was disconnecting everyone's earphones and headed toward the mystery guest.

He looked at me bewilderedly.

"Are you supposed to be here?"

"Who are you?"

"The teacher."

"Oh."

"Are you new?"

"I'm fifteen."

"Is this your class?"

He shrugged and stared at the screen. I tried another angle.

"What's your name?"

"Duane."

"What are you doing?"

"Watchin' TV."

"Duane, the TV is off."

"I know. I see the picture better that way."

"Are you supposed to be here? This is reading lab."

He pulled a crumpled schedule out of his pocket. He was in the right place.

"Duane, come let me fix you up a folder."

"At the commercial."

"No, now."

He tapped every object on the way to the back of the room, including Cha Cha Ramirez's blue knit hat, which brought Chummy and Cheeks, his best friends, to their feet with clenched fists.

"Hey pinche gringo, you touch Cha Cha and I break your ass."

Duane grinned back.

"You play five-card stud?"

Cheeks grabbed him by the shirt. "Brown Sensations rule, cavrone!"

I grabbed Duane this time. "What is your full name?"

"Duane Down and Dirty, teacher."

"Are you new?"

"What to?"

"Here."

He took a deck of cards out of his pocket and shuffled them with a dexterity before which an experienced dealer would have genuflected.

"Duane, what grade are you in?"

He laid two cards down for each of us.

"Twenty-one, double or nothing."

"What grade?"

The ripple of the deck caught everyone's attention. He loved it. He stood up and performed feats of legerdemain with fifty-two vulgarly illustrated cards. Each facade was decorated with a scantily clad Dolly Parton in boots and petal curls.

I got zero information, but the kids got a magnificent display of manual dexterity and huckster hype. "Down and dirty." He flipped them all backwards into a neat pile.

"Smoke 'em if you got 'em." This time a fan of extraordinary proportion.

Class ended before he could show us his finale.

Ruth Lescovak told me she thought Duane was cute. She was an adorable child whose brain had been damaged by a bad fall when she was eleven. She loved Paddington Bear books and Holly Hobbie cards and, as time progressed, Duane.

I found him in front of the set every class period.

He would translate his viewings to Ruth, who sat next to him on the floor.

"It's *Gunsmoke* now, and Miss Kitty just threw a rustler out of the saloon."

Ruth nodded and smiled.

"Matt Dillon can fight but he loses at cards."

I asked everyone to settle down. Nobody paid attention. Cha Cha turned up the tape recorder where Santana drummed out "Evil Ways."

Duane jumped to his feet and circled the Listening Center. "Pick a card, any card."

Cheeks reached for a card.

Manuel Hogan elbowed him. "*Mira qué tetas.*"

It was the deuce of diamonds, represented by a top-heavy Polynesian woman with her hands on her hips.

"Hit me again."

"Qué?"

"Put it back in the deck."

He flipped and flopped the cards in an accordion rainbow of changing places. He plunked the deck on the table.

"Cut."

Cha Cha divided the stack in half. Duane picked them up, rippled the cards up, down, around, and over, fanned them out and whisked the two of diamonds out and flashed it one inch from Cheeks's face.

It was pretty impressive.

"Lay your money down, boys. Daddy's gonna take you to town."

They coughed up lunch money.

I intervened with my gambling-is-illegal rap. No one paid the slightest attention.

"Jokers are wild, but jacks are better."

There were quarters everywhere.

"Dealer takes two."

I don't understand what happened next, except that Duane collected all the money like a veteran croupier and Leland Gowers screamed something about "his two burritos and chocolate milk." Duane grinned at the group and yelled out, "Low ball."

I assumed it was a derisive term implying some inadequacy with a testicle.

Leland gave Chummy a shove.

Cha Cha kicked Matthew, who protects Leland from what he calls the "Beaner Gangs."

It was quite a brawl. Tape recorders sailed across the tables, chairs became airborne, screams escalated, including my own, and punches made dropped-melon sounds. Furniture turned and rolled, the top of the Stories of Interest table was swept clean in a flurry of flying motivational material.

Duane jumped up on a table to calm the crowd.

"Let's watch TV. Turn it off!"

He repeated that several times.

Leland was the first to answer him as he ducked a thesaurus on his right.

"It's off, asshole. What's on?"

Duane glared at the set.

"Hogan's Heroes."

"Do you just get one station?"

"Get offa that table or I'll knock you into the middle of next week!"

It was a football coach who taught Health Education next door. I had once listened in amazement when he gave a fifteen-minute dissertation on the benefits of oatmeal.

"Looks like you've got a few pukes here. Pick up those chairs!"

He shrieked orders at everyone. I was horrified at his bullish manner, but thankful for his interruption. Normally I handle all chaos with my own convoluted form of discipline. This situation had turned into a physical fracas and someone could have been injured.

"You over there, put those tables upright!"

Previously inert students jumped to attention and started arranging furniture. The Chicanos hissed silently, but they put the room back in order.

Duane was still on the table asking people to turn off the TV.

Coach Donalds heaved a final warning.

"Get your ass offa the table before I kick it."

Ruth gently tapped Coach Donalds's arm. "Don't get mad at Duane, he's watching TV."

"The TV's off, little sister, and he's on the table."

"He'll get off when he wants to play cards."

I thanked the coach for his help and assured him I could take it from there. Ruth walked him to the door. "Duane sees things, but he doesn't hurt."

The kids sat quietly except for the barrio boys, who plotted how the Brown Sensations would get revenge on the gringo who wouldn't coach soccer.

Duane still stood staring at the screen.

I took inventory on broken machinery. The sweeping panoramic estimate was clearly in the thousands.

Ten minutes to go till the bell. Nowhere to go but back to basics.

Duane shifted his gaze to the Viewmate Center.

"Momma needs a new pair of shoes."

"Is your show over?" Ruth asked him.

"Who'll go the game, c'mon sailors, bets up front, money on the table."

"How can we put money on the table if you're on it?" said Ruth.

He got down and placed his cards in two neat piles. He fanned them together and backed up the other way. The bell rang and he walked past the TV, watched for a minute, and left.

We lived fairly comfortably that semester. The tape decks were used daily for punk and soul. We struck up a deal. They got to listen while they read a book.

The vocabulary machines did their split-second castanet sambas to no one in particular. We used the guided readers for group exercises after which the winner got to play five-card stud with Duane. The workbooks gathered dust and the tachistoscope was placed behind the television set that Duane watched from time to time when it was off.

The hyperactive kids sat still long enough to learn black-jack. The Chicanos stopped asking Duane if he did ovens and washing machines. They also taught us the words to "Quiere Tu." The three mentally retarded kids put down the encyclopedias long enough to learn Go Fish and Old Maid.

Leland taught Cha Cha Ramirez the names of all the Green Bay Packers.

I lied about the end-of-semester evaluation tests and said I lost them. John Flansbaum came to make a periodic inspection and found out our secrets.

He railed about abuse of equipment.

He raged on about capital outlay and waste.

He stormed a stuffy tirade about the inability to make a silk purse out of a sow's ear.

Ruth told him that he was disturbing Duane, who was watching *Bewitched.*

He sniffed out the door in a hayfever huff, mumbling that forty thousand dollars was a lot of money.

The average house in this area runs about eighty thousand dollars. We created a home for half that, electricity not included.

All in all, it was a wise investment.

Song of Sappho

The summer I was fourteen, my hormones, like all of my friends', were in a rage. For our entire ninth grade year we had talked of sex and love, romance and petting, hickies and blue balls, until we were sufficiently worked into a frenzy. Judy Howard and I had made a firm resolve to do something about it. Our goal was to experience being French-kissed and felt up by September 13, back-to-school day. This was no easy task. First of all, we were not the pert-nosed blond and chirpy types who got asked to dance at junior high. We were the girls who had a stash of Maybelline medium-brown eyebrow pencils, Coty pressed translucent powder, and tubes of Pink Heaven lipstick in our lockers and a permanent rendezvous in the girls' restroom by the Science wing each morning to apply them. We'd carried nickels in our purses ever since we saw *It's Wonderful Being a Girl* in the sixth grade. Judy got her period way before I did, but I lied and said I had mine six months after she'd started.

We had categorized sexual activity into two major divisions. There was "above the waist," which consisted of hand goodies on your chest and surrounding area, hickies and hard kisses on the neck and shoulder, hair caressing, ear blowing, and soul kissing. "Below the waist" was infinitely more serious. Finally, at the end of August, we made a date with two cadets from military school to go to the movies. But in truth, we were there to make out and experiment from the waist up.

They were punctual and polite. Pete was blond, cute, tan, and he spoke with a slight lisp. Al was another matter. He was dark, short, with a huge hooked nose and funny bluish lips. I couldn't pronounce his last name, and when he turned to his buddy I fixated on the birthmark on his left cheek. It looked like a topographic map of the island of Kauai. He reeked of Old Spice and Colgate-with-Gardol toothpaste.

Judy had already gone in, delighted with her *objet d'amour.*

I slouched inside, walking slightly ahead so no one would pair me with Al. We found a quiet corner and pretended to watch the film. I could not find Judy. Al inched his hand along the back of the chair. It touched my ponytail and I jumped. He withdrew and started in again. I was studying Sandra Dee for details of fashion. His hand had reached my shoulder. He squeezed it ever so slightly and put his bristly head on my neck. It felt curiously warm and tickly. I pretended he was John Saxon or Sal Mineo, and it felt better. I remember him blowing hot toothpaste-smelling air in my ear and I got goosebumps. By the time Sandra Dee was ready to reconcile with her dying mother, Al had kissed my cheeks and, after several furtive attempts, my mouth. I loved it. He wanted to kiss long and hard, but I couldn't hold my breath any longer. I didn't think it was proper or possible to inhale in an embrace. He whispered for me to "relax," and kissed me again with his tongue. I tried to evaluate if I was repulsed. I thought about germs and spit, but the sensation won out. It felt terrific, and he did taste like toothpaste. We kissed and kissed. His hand inched its way past my shoulder, around my back, and on the side of my minuscule left breast. He held his palm perfectly still in a demicup position. I could feel his body heat through my dyed-to-match sweater. Ever so slowly he snaked his hand over the crest and my nipple rose to meet its first brush with hand goodies.

I faintly recall Sandra Dee running after a coffin in the streets, sobbing "I'm sorry, I'm sorry." I was in a frenzy of new emotions at fever pitch. The house lights brought me back to reality. Al wanted to hold my hand, but I wouldn't let him. Judy and I walked to the roller rink alone and called our parents. We waited in nervous silence, which she broke first.

"Did you do it?"

I nodded a guilty yes and quickly asked her the same. She did it too.

"Do you think anyone will know?"

"I won't tell if you won't."

We made our secret pact just as my father pulled up in his green Chevy Delray.

I obsessed about my initiation for weeks, replaying the tapes in my head with a mixture of guilt and excitement. I had crossed the imaginot line and the pain was excruciating. My coming of sexual age left me confused and guilt-ridden and in constant quest for more. I kept my shameful lust to myself, but I suspected others knew and thought me cheap. The cult of the good girl had a profound effect on all of us. We experienced our passionate longings in private parked cars and dark rooms while denying all of it and denouncing any girl who allegedly let someone handle her. We bound ourselves to the cruel double standard.

Walking onto a high school campus today would horrify the righteous and repressed. Couples openly fondle each other, hand-holding in class goes unremarked; in some circles virginity is the mark of an outcast. Lunch-hour trysts produce more passion over potato chips than we knew at the deliberately orchestrated make-out parties of our adolescence.

Sometimes I feel silently envious of my students' capacity to be so free from others' moral constraints. The gawky, insecure junior high kid groveling to make the first awkward gesture of love is my soulmate, not the happy hedonists of high school.

All this "new morality," however, is strictly reserved for heterosexual couples. In one dreary education course we were asked to memorize Erikson's analysis of adolescence as the quest for identity. We hashed over peer pressure, rebellion, conformity, sexual experimentation, group comparisons of codes and conduct. Not once was the notion of homosexuality even suggested.

For those teenagers whose homosexual preference has been secretly acknowledged, adolescence is anything but gay.

Consider the semantics of derision. Anything that is hideous is "gay," a social outcast is a "fag," an ugly girl a "lesbo," a sensitive boy a "fairy." Male friends who spend too much time together are "homos." Any girl who openly supports Women's Lib is a "dyke." Hostility surrounds the recipients of these labels. They are talked about, mercilessly teased, and silently scorned. In Peter Fisher's excellent book *The Gay Mystique*, he describes the inner sexual makeup as the dominant focus during adolescence. He informs us that social disapproval of homosexuality is so frightening that gay teenagers often demonstrate exaggerated heterosexual behavior in an attempt to distract themselves and others from their real preference.

This was certainly the case with Jayne. She was one of those dark, exotic beauties that Gauguin would have painted in a reclining pose. She had a languid air about her; tall and sensual, she would literally drape herself across a desk.

She was the youngest child of a prominent family with vast property holdings, staunch conservative values, and clearly one of the most tyrannically offensive fathers in the history of arrogance. He was an outspoken critic of the schools, the community, the Mexican problem (his words), the loss of law and order, the lack of patriotism, and the laziness of public servants. He judged the qualities of a good teacher by interesting rules. Males who coached Little League were dedicated teachers; females whose homes ran as well as their classes got his seal of approval. We were subjected to his opinion on every issue, from selected reading materials in Social Studies to the appropriation of funds for girls' sports.

Jayne hated his guts, a fact she shared with anyone who would listen. "My dad's a butt, and my mom's an ass for staying with him." Most of us found her analysis quite accurate.

Jayne had the dubious reputation of being "an easy mark." Uneasy tales of her sexual behavior buzzed from classroom to classroom after every weekend. Twenty guys were said to have had her in a closet at an all-night party in her dad's cabin; it was rumored she had offered herself to the star football player as recompense for his injured knee; half of the Chicanos on the soccer team claimed to have scored; and there were speculations about the nature of her relationships with certain coaches.

She seemed unaffected by it all. Her father, on the other hand, handed down restriction after restriction. Jayne would placidly comply and go right on with her activities.

She had an understated sense of humor that matched the general phlegmatic aspect of her personality. I didn't know for a long time that this rather flat affect was directly related to her heavy dependence on barbiturates.

I found out the hard way. She overdosed in my class.

We sent for the paramedics as she lay unconscious on the floor by the science fiction bookrack. Her breathing was labored and her eyelids fluttered. I was terrified that she would die. They pumped her stomach at the hospital. She was sent home safe and unsound that evening.

It turned out to be my fault. Her father had me hauled into the principal's office to be railed at, lectured to, and warned.

He yelled for fifteen minutes on the slacking off of those with tenure, the lameness of the administration for not controlling the use of dangerous drugs, and the evil influence of rock music on the values of the nuclear family. It was an absurd tirade, replete with rage and helplessness. I didn't even bother responding to his faulty logic.

She was in the classroom, listlessly looking at the art prints on the wall. She heard my footsteps, but did not turn around.

"He's a real prince of peace, isn't he?"

"He's a royal pain in the ass, if you want my honest opinion. Jayne, what in hell did you do that for?"

"I like to be mellow."

"Terrific, but you might wind up dead." Not terribly deep, but I was still furious.

"I'm careful with my sources, if that's what you mean."

"You're not that careful, if you o.d."

"That was a mistake."

"Indeed."

I was too cranky to lecture her. There are times when I feel that kids get what they deserve and should take care of themselves.

She held out a book and asked me if I'd read it. Its title was *Sappho Was a Right-On Woman.*

"I think it's a righteous work. My mom thought it was a book on Greek mythology."

It occurred to me that she was probably flirting with the bisexual chic currently in vogue with movie stars and David Bowie groupies. I handed it back to her with a warning that she should keep it away from her father.

"Will you read it and tell me what you think?"

"Jayne, I'm awfully busy with other stuff right now."

"Please."

The tone of her "please" bull's-eyed my incapacity to say no without guilt, only mildly altered by years of therapy.

I took it, but I said I would read it only if I found the time.

She behaved better after that. She contributed to class discussions, handed in her homework, and read the assignments. She actually looked like she had an activated metabolism.

My enthusiasm was short-lived. She got busted in P. E. for selling pills. Her newfound energy was her switch to speed.

Her father demanded the dismissal of her gym teacher for negligence. The school decided not to prosecute, but to assign her to one of the "counselors." These mini-therapists were interns from a local university with field work to finish for a degree in psychology. The bulk of them were laboriously self-conscious and equally ill-read. Jayne's "therapist" was a guy who wore clogs, dabbled in auras, believed in open marriage, and thought *Star Trek* was a Jungian statement about the twentieth century.

Jayne would sit and fiddle with her hair as he encouraged her to "rap."

I read the book during a bout of the flu. I admired the author's stand on lesbianism, but found the bias a bit too proselytizing.

Jayne lolled around after class the day I came back, drawing beach scenes on her binder.

"Did you read it?"

"Yes. I liked it, even if it was a little preachy."

"Do you think gays are sick?"

"No more than the rest of us."

"I think I'm pregnant."

"What?"

"My period's late and Duncan won't take me to the clinic."

Duncan was the surfer king of the beachy set. He had a fabulous body, a terrific smile, a goony sense of humor, and a mind filled with saline.

"Do you need a ride?"

"No, I have a car."

"Then you should find out immediately."

I cringed at the idea of her father handling that dilemma. He'd sue Duncan, kill her, and blame us for encouraging adolescents to fornicate by giving them sex education.

None of what she had told me was true.

The phone rang in the middle of the night. It was Jayne,

sobbing hysterically. There was a clamor in the background that was deafening. She asked if I would come and get her, and gave me the address.

Against my better judgment, I drove down the coast to a shopping center in a beach town. The place turned out to be a bowling alley on top of a pizza parlor. I parked and went up the urine-smelling stairs of the Strike Out Bowl.

She was sitting by the ball checkout counter, crying into her hands. There was an odd feeling about this place, in addition to the general sleaziness of cracking paint and stale smoke. I couldn't make sense of her words. Something about Crystal and never again. I suggested we go to my car. Hundreds of hostile eyes watched this transaction. It took a minute to realize they were all female. I guess I didn't expect to see so many women in a bowling alley at two in the morning. Most of them looked like the Safeway shoppers and station wagon schleppers of the suburbs. I was not a welcome guest.

Jayne crouched against the door and choked and sobbed.

"Do your parents know where you are?"

"Fuck no."

"Are you upset because you are pregnant?"

She cried harder, so I assumed that meant yes.

"Who is Crystal?"

"My lover."

I didn't say anything.

"She's not anymore. I got dumped on my ass tonight."

"I'm sorry."

"I'm not pregnant. Besides, Duncan's a geek."

I agreed with her.

"Shall I take you home?" I had already decided to drop her off a block away.

"Yeah. They think I'm at a friend's. I'll tell them she wanted to drink, so I left. He'll like that."

I pulled over about six houses down from hers. She thanked me and started to get out.

"Don't tell anybody, will you?"

I promised I wouldn't. I wasn't exactly sure what I shouldn't tell.

On her seventeenth birthday, she ran away and moved in with a thirty-year-old woman named Babs who ran a gay bar at the beach. It took a while for her family to find her. She refused to come home and declared her happiness at coming clean.

He had them both arrested.

Her father, at the request of a psychiatrist, had her transferred to seventy-two-hour-hold at County for observation and testing.

She was released to her parents' custody. They hired a home tutor and forced her into therapy with a man who specialized in systematic desensitization and aversion therapy. She got her diploma in June. They let her march with her class, took her out to dinner, and whisked her home for the summer.

She tutored kids in Spanish and coached for the Bobby Sox, the girls' Little League. They screened her phone calls, monitored her activities, and scrutinized her contacts. The psychiatrist felt successful and, from what I understand, is using her case as a journal article for the A. P. A. quarterly.

There was a garden party written up in the paper to celebrate her eighteenth birthday. In the accompanying photo, she was slicing the tiered cake and smiling.

That afternoon she joined the Marines. She has been to Guam, Hawaii, the Philippines, Japan, and is currently stationed in North Carolina working as a counselor in the Human Relations Program at Cherry Point. She writes me that she is happy and feels purposeful.

She has helped relocate Vietnamese families and has been approached about becoming an 02 intelligence field officer because of her language ability. Her last card was from Billy Carter's gas station, where she was vacationing with a Julie.

> I cannot be open within the rank and file but I'm up front with myself and I like it.

She signed it Lavender Jayne.

Woe Is Me at Wounded Knee

Looking back and trying to figure out where my peer group got its information about minority groups, one thing is quite clear. Any contribution from school was negligible.

I heard the word *integration* for the first time when I was in junior high. I did not know what it meant. I have a vague recollection of some black and white photos about it in *Life* magazine.

There was an even greater paucity of information regarding the American Indian. We learned that "friendly redskins" said "how" for hello, lived in tepees with an opening in the top to let the smoke out, and put one dead fish in the hole when planting corn.

Tonto said "Kemosabe."

A playmate of my brother's told me every morbid detail of scalping.

We moved to California in 1955. I heard the word

Mexican for the first time in my life. It was always followed by such ominous definitions that I refused to go to school. Mexicans carried switchblades in their hair, beat you up, pantsed you, smeared you with lipstick, then put you in a trash can. I was frozen with terror at the prospect of being near them.

I tried to skulk around the halls unnoticed. I avoided the lunch tables where these brown-skinned *pachucos* sat waiting to get me. I kept my eyes downward, but I would tense up at the sight of those funny white shoes the girls wore, called bunnies.

The second day in my new school class, Juanita Flores came up and shoved my flat chest.

"I hear you don't like me cuz I don't got no mother."

I remember trying to talk but only managing to cry.

In homeroom, I was put in alphabetical order in front of Chon Garcia, who called me Chi Chi Pancakes and exposed himself when the teacher wasn't looking.

I cried every day for the first quarter.

By Christmas my terror had subsided somewhat, and Lydia Gomez and I were friends. I never went to her house. She never came to mine. We ignored each other's history and lived on the neutral terrain of milk break and lunch. How much we could have learned from our cultural differences. We never spoke of them, though; that's just the way it was.

Thirteen years later Lydia was working for Chavez in Davis and I was student-teaching in an inner-city school where 80 percent of the population spoke Spanish and only one counselor could converse with them in their native tongue.

One day, news of a special assembly circulated like a storm warning. The kids had declared Chicano Pride Week. Monday morning an ornate entourage of lowered, brightly decorated cars had pulled up in front of the school to let out the self-appointed leaders of the week's activities. Costumes from all parts of Mexico were paraded through the halls. Beautiful displays of color, culture, and custom had been organized for every free period.

We saw regional dances, traditional ceremonies, wedding festivities, even a mock bullfight. It was an impressive education.

The students piled into the auditorium and in a matter of minutes the place was packed. The invisible energy level reverberated wall to wall.

A young girl with a red hibiscus in her long black hair took the microphone and screamed an angry proclamation.

"My name is Carmen. I am a Mexican. This is my school too. We deserve a better education."

Roars of applause came up from the floor.

"We want these demands met now!"

Her list of grievances was logical, well thought out, and articulate. More Spanish-speaking staff, a curriculum sensitive to cultural needs, less gringo food in the cafeteria, better student relations.

She came on like a mini Dolores Huerta, and the crowd went crazy.

Except for the principal, Commander Silver, U. S. N., retired, who stood at ease squinting at the stage.

She'd saved the best for last.

Rodney Wooford, self-proclaimed "biggest bad black ass on campus," joined her on the stage. She didn't introduce him; she just waited while he made his way to the microphone. He took his time, looking from side to side, adjusting his beret, and finally staring into the crowd until he had them quiet and only slightly paranoid.

Relations between the blacks and Chicanos had been strained and upon occasion violent. Stabbings in P. E. were not infrequent. Police were stationed on campus to patrol activities before and after school. Rodney had been expelled four times for fighting. He belonged to the local chapter of the Black Panthers; his trademark was one black leather glove, which he would "dare" people to remove. Four tried. Four failed.

"Mosta the time we don't get along, you dig, but we had meetings."

Everybody listened to Rodney.

"This place here needs some changes bad, know what I mean? Mosta the time black and brown are at war. On this one we are together."

He raised his fist into the air and in his best accent yelled out *"Viva la raza!"* And he and Carmen put their arms around each other.

The din of applause was deafening. I remember having chills.

It was a microcosmic dream for the disillusioned sixties

survivors, many of whom were manning their stations in the auditorium.

All this by way of introducing the flip side of newly awakened consciousness.

The group movements of the last two decades have brought about much-needed change. Some would argue not enough, but the genesis is there. Even the most tight-minded diehards of tradition are aware of Affirmative Action.

However.

Sometimes the causes cross and conflict. Most of us have had to sift through our arsenals of allegiances to assess priorities. Should a gay black male take precedence over a lesbian Polish-American senior citizen, or are the rights of the handicapped being isolated here?

Heightened consciousness causes enlightened confusion in some cases. Steinbeck talked about those who get crushed under wheels of social change.

He should have known Chavela Sanchez.

Chavela, four feet eleven inches of solid muscle. Raven-haired, flat-faced daughter of a hard-drinking Mexican car mechanic who ignored his Indian blood like his wife ignored his illegitimate offspring who populated the neighborhood. Mrs. Sanchez was a weary woman. Chavela's five older brothers had caused her so much grief from hassles with the law, gang fighting, drug pushing, and property destruction that by the time Chavela reached puberty, she was just too tired to deal with her.

Chavela knew that and accommodated her by being

impossible. She'd been expelled from every elementary school in the area by the time she was eight. The nuns at the local parish thought she was possessed. The priests avoided her. The police wished they could. She was a polished delinquent.

Chavela threw rocks at people out of meanness, dared anyone to try and kick her ass. Her fists remained constantly clenched just in case. How she made it to high school is anybody's guess.

The matchmaker counselor put her in my Women's Studies class because she "looks tough, like she can take it."

He brought her to my class to introduce her to me. She eyed me suspiciously and gave a slight upward tilt of her head to signify hello.

"Where are the guys in here?"

I did my best to explain why I had difficulty getting them to sign up.

"What is this class, man, dyke shit?"

"No, Chavela, we are restudying history to include the contributions of women."

"Where are the Mexicans, man?"

"We cover Mexican women, if that's what you mean."

"I'll kick anybody's ass who has bad things to say about Chicanos, man." She rapped her knuckles on the desk, then threw punches into her palm like a pitcher warming up with a mitt. "I probably won't stay around, man."

She kicked a chair out with her foot and sat down.

She was suspended that afternoon for punching out a cheerleader chanting "We've got a team that's on the beam."

Chavela thought she said "bean," which meant "beaner," which meant war.

Her father came to get her in a rum stupor, knocked her across the office, called her a *puta*, and dragged her into his truck.

She was back the next week. She had to be in all her classes or she risked being expelled, so she showed up.

I was giving a fiery defense of the E. R. A., none too subtle and not the least bit objective. I tried to relate to their reality bases—independence, money, abortion, freedom from discrimination, equality in love, and an end to patriarchal tyranny. I used the double standard of brother's and sister's behavior. I talked about bossy fathers and passive mothers.

Chavela stood up before the end of class, declared herself a women's libber, and waged war on machismo.

She was suspended again for bursting into the boys' locker room and shouting, "Fucking pigs, I'll kick your ass too if you don't give me my rights!"

She got a black eye from her father and a warning from the school that she was fast approaching Last Chance Saloon.

"He's a chauvinist pig pinche, like my father."

She pronounced the *ch* while denouncing the vice-principal, who was exactly as she described him.

Her presence in class was a curious addition, welcomed with delight as well as dread.

When we read about the early heroines of the suffrage

movement, Chavela would curse their opposition. She thought Susan B. Anthony should have learned street fighting and declared she would have stood guard at Seneca Falls: "If those pigs tried to get in, I'd of flattened their gringo asses."

She identified with Mother Jones, "tough chick who knew where it was at," but didn't know what to think of Margaret Sanger. Her Catholic education made her wary until she learned that Sanger spent time in jail.

"Okay, the chick's okay. Cops are pigs anyhow."

She got in trouble with her Chicano friends, who were mad because she made the guys mad. If a Mexican boy made the mistake of whistling or catcalling, Chavela socked him. She criticized her Mexican girl friends for wearing makeup, for doing all the work for their boyfriends, and "for putting out to macho oppression."

They all avoided Chavela. Her teachers cautiously put the he/she option into sentences. She'd stop people in the halls and ask them if they were for the E. R. A.

Most thought it was an athletic team.

Those who approved got a friendly punch on the arm and a "right on." Those who said no got decked.

Her mother worried about her militancy. Her father was too drunk to notice. He went on a binge mid-semester and disappeared for two months.

History dealt Chavela a dirty hand. Mr. Sanchez's hiatus found him on an Arizona highway, semicomatose, with a blown-out engine and no money. The samaritan who found him was on his way to Wounded Knee in behalf of a Native American club. He took Sanchez with him.

Mr. Sanchez did a sixty-day turnaround and found his Indian roots. He returned home sober, proud, and determined that after all these years of hiding he would weep no more forever.

He'd pulled into town on a Sunday and called a family council. In zealous tones he spoke of proud Navajo tradition. He announced that certain changes in the home life would take place shortly. He excused his children one at a time so he could be alone with Mrs. Sanchez, who was still tired but bewildered.

Chavela recounted the story to the class on Monday. She'd found her own definition of this behavior. "The guy's got the d.t.'s from all the booze he's been drinkin'."

The next week Chavela didn't wait for roll to be taken. She galloped to the front of the room and signaled for silence.

"Check this. The guy thinks he's Billy Jack. I'm supposed to call him Crashing Thunder. He named my old lady Distant Flashing Standing."

Her eyes waited for our amused chortles before they clouded with seriousness.

"He told me he'd knock hell outa me if I call her Mom. He named all my brothers, but they told him to shine it."

Several girls snickered in spiteful glee. Chavela was getting hers and they were delighted. She neglected to share her new name, Wolf Lily, which Mr. Sanchez had made up because Chavela was born around Easter.

The saga continued. Apparently Mrs. Sanchez went along with her husband's conversion, since it meant he'd stay sober. She braided her hair, wore turquoise jewelry, and tried to convince Chavela to do the same. Chavela refused and her father roughed her up and told her scare stories about disobedient daughters.

"The dude's gone, man. Now we can't even eat. I come home the other day and there's no dinner. My mom puts black coal all over my face and says we're gonna fast for visions."

We were spellbound by this one. The girls in the class found this ritual bizarre, although easily half of them came to school with black smudges on their foreheads every Ash Wednesday.

Chavela described their new culinary adventures.

"I'm dyin for a burrito and she's supposed to be cookin' muskrats and water-lily roots. Should I call the pigs on him?"

I was tempted to suggest Community Mental Health Center, but she couldn't prove anything. Crashing Thunder was her legal guardian and Distant Flashing Standing was there to make a house a tepee.

They did rain dances in the living room. They chanted at the moon in the evenings. They gathered around the burning embers in the barbecue to discuss family matters. Crashing Thunder studied up on tradition. Chavela's menses were his next obsession. He found out her menstrual cycle from his wife, who found it out from the depleting Tampax box snuggled behind the Kleenex in the closet. Crashing Thunder locked Chavela in her room and carefully explained to his Distant Flashing Standing why this move was so crucial.

"My mother comes up to me," Chavela told us when she came back, "and whispers that we have to talk about being unclean. She tells me that when this happens, you should run in the woods and hide. But since we live here I should go to my room."

Nobody laughed at this confession. We had discussed menstrual taboos and insecurities. This situation sounded oddly like Victorian mythology, where you took to your bed and were quietly indisposed.

"She says that if you look at a man when you are like that, you'll contaminate his blood. I told her that was loco, but she slapped me and told me to mind my father."

We proposed some counterattacks. Mandy Oliver suggested that she compose a Tampon Tango and step her way through the neighborhood spreading blood disease in all males by passing out samples of the monthly cotton plug.

Christine Watson thought the parish priest could help.

Beverly Littleton suggested that the nurse intervene.

Tina Bowers said Crashing Thunder should be committed. Chavela thought she should "get up a gang and beat the shit out of him."

She was absent the entire week of her next period.

She lumbered in late, arms curved and hanging in simian stance. She punched each desk and swore as she ankled to her seat.

"Shit, fuck, cavrone, asshole!"

I was in a foul humor and was not amused at her interrupting a lecture on Rosie the Riveter. She disregarded my request that she sit down.

"I'm gettin married to a bad soldier."

"Running away with a marine is hardly the answer."

"Man, you don't understand. Bad soldier means fierce soldier, and he's my husband cuz my father arranged it."

"Chavela, are you serious?"

"What? Ya think I'm gonna joke about some dude in Arizona I ain't never seen who's supposed to marry me?"

An outraged Julie Miller spoke up spontaneously. "He can't do that. Let's call the cops."

"What's the charge?"

"Kidnapping."

"He's her father."

"Okay, then, get the Arizona police alerted. There has to be a law about forced marriage."

"The guy's family lives on a reservation."

"So what?"

"Indian law rules."

She told us that her mother had informed her of the plans and she had said no. Her mother did not get angry; instead, she started to chant and jump around the kitchen. When she calmed down, she dipped her hands into a bowl of salted water and put them on Chavela's shoulders.

"I prize you very much, but this cannot be helped."

Chavela threw a fit and several pieces of furniture. Her father rushed in and knocked her out cold. Mrs. Sanchez put her to bed with a couple of clandestine Hail Marys.

She checked out of school on a Friday. The reason for withdrawal was a clearly stated "marriage."

She ran away at Barstow, on the Arizona border, sneaking out the window of the ladies' room of the Shell station. She hid out with friends, but the law forced her to go home.

Determined to go through with this marriage, Crashing Thunder set out for the reservation with her. Chavela ditched out at Flagstaff. He blackened both her eyes for that escape.

Apparently they made it the third time, assisted by some of her brothers.

Chavela was back in a week—unmarked, unscathed, and unabated.

"You wouldn't believe the shit my father thought I should marry. Bad soldier was more like a bad dream."

This feudal drama had us all mesmerized. We were after details. Chavela's descriptive abilities were limited.

"The guy's ugly, buncha zits everywhere and real bossy type."

She giggled to herself. "He tells me all this pain in the ass stuff about how bad he is and how he's supposed to be a big macho and I'm supposed to be his Navajo Novia."

"How did you get out?"

"I told him I was a *puta.* Then he didn't want me."

She grinned from ear to ear, and so did we.

The Vatican Connection

There is a woman in New Mexico who found Jesus on a tortilla. She was rolling her husband's burrito when she noticed something that looked like a face. She reported that she had chills all over her body as the mournful, romantic Jesus with a wreath of thorns on his shoulder-length hair stared back at her.

The parish priest, a hard-drinking, somewhat cynical Irishman, proceeded cautiously, since miracles need to be investigated; but he agreed to bless the tortilla.

The woman encased the wafer-sized image in a glass case and titled it "Jesus on a Tortilla." She has built a little shrine decorated with holy pictures, flowers, and burning candles. Over eight thousand people have passed through her house to view the apparition. Several meanings have been attached, invented, and interpreted.

The archbishop politely suggested that the whole incident was an accident. The woman ignored this completely.

"It's my miracle and it has changed my life."

She told the press, "I do not know why this has happened to me, but God has come into my life through this tortilla."

I believe that she believes it. What is a miracle to some represents a psychotic hallucination to another. The rightness or wrongness of the interpretation is probably irrelevant, since it's essentially a question of faith or illusion, which are possibly the same thing.

A belief system based on abstractions which defy logic is such a complex entity that in principle I support Madeline O'Hare's forceful proposition that religion has no place in the schools.

Teachers have no business imposing spiritual dogma on kids. Students should refrain from foisting their brand of devotion on their peers and instructors.

The irony, of course, is that people are their beliefs. Perhaps the issue is tolerance.

The rebirth of religiosity in recent years was both predictable and timely. Post-Vietnam depression followed up by a widespread barbiturate haze naturally dovetailed into the metaphysical odyssey of the early seventies. One now looks for answers, not questions.

Eldridge Cleaver witnesses for Christ.

Richard Alpert became Baba Ram Dass, Hindu servant of God.

Larry Flynt's conversion made world-wide news.

There is an odd comfort derived from a spiritually defined person. John is a Mormon, Peter is Catholic, and Rachel is Jewish. Neatly drawn lines where one deals with givens.

Can intellectual growth ever leave these superstructures behind and proceed without them?

I wonder.

Does a person's religious core alter how he defines issues and ideas?

I think so.

That is why keeping religion out of the schools is a rhetorical impossibility.

I learned just how difficult, when I bumped lives with little Marco Califano, tiny transplant from Hackensack, New Jersey. He had curly black hair, culture shock, and a fat case of schoolphobia.

Back east, he had known everyone in his parochial-school class since kindergaren. Now he was in a progressive middle school in California where military dependents were the bulk of the student body and his teachers wore jeans.

He hated it.

He begged his parents to send him to another parochial school or send him back home.

They refused to do either.

His mother brought him to the counselor's office, where he stayed for the first three weeks of school. Mrs. Pines, the counselor, thought he should "feel out where he was coming from." She reminded us that "you can't push Virgo men."

Her business was supposed to be counseling kids, but in

reality her office was a haven where she wrote her esoteric papers for the progressive university she attended in the evenings.

A word about Mrs. Pines. She was the sort of breathlessly manic overachiever one often finds in education. With only an elementary-education credential, she was convinced that she alone knew what was right for kids.

Most of the staff avoided her. She had a particular squint to her eyes that she would affect when asked the simplest question. You would think she was about to offer a peace plan for the Middle East. Depending upon which course she was taking at the moment, you would get a treatise on the subject of your question and an educational lecture on why her perspective was relevant.

In the two years I'd worked there, Mrs. Pines had woven Parapsychology, Astrology, Holistic Health, Auras-Reading, and Psychic Ability into the junior high curriculum.

The kids wouldn't go to her unless forced. Apparently she questioned them about place and exact time of birth before finding a proper course of study. She found the class offerings unenlightened, and most of us "rigidly intellectual." When a staff member was annoyed by her pretentious palavering, she would smile and say in gushes of cultivated warmth, "Perhaps you're not ready to hear this yet."

She cornered me once at a party and told me that her mission in life was to deal with great philosophical issues.

Poor Marco went unknown and unscheduled while she philosophized.

His mother finally called to meet his teachers, and Mrs.

Pines got him enrolled in some classes before the Cancerian Mrs. Califano, "so detailed and precise," got to campus.

She was panting and squinting when she brought him to my room.

"Marco, this is your teacher."

She whispered to me in semiconfidentiality, "He's a Virgo, not quite in tune with the vibes here. I suppose he's gifted, but IQ scores don't measure creativity."

I thanked her.

I welcomed Marco; he shook my hand and said, "How do you do." He crouched in a corner and didn't say much.

The kids teased him because of his untanned, dead white skin.

"Hey, snowball, give us a break."

"Don't they have sun in Boston?"

Marco folded his hands and corrected them. "New Jersey; dontcha know anything?"

His accent was broad and pronounced.

"Listen, Ivory Flakes, you want to borrow my Coppertone?"

"Shad up."

I told them to shut up also. This was an accelerated group of rambunctious ninth graders assembled for ninety minutes of Basic Education. Most of them were from military homes where fathers were gone for months at a time. Their mothers tended to be depressed or coped by drinking or taking lovers. They were a rowdy crew with angry energy and little interest in school.

"I hate this goddamn class."

Marco shifted his erect body around to find the culprit.

"Don't tawk like that in fronta the ladies."

"Are you a fag?"

"Ain't you got no manners?"

"Aw, Jesus Christ."

"Don't take the Lord's name in vain."

"Eat it, woman."

"These people are savages. At my other school people didn't act like this."

"Your other school was full of pussies."

"My old man says East Coast sucks. He sucks my mother."

Marco looked horrified and stiffly let Rocky know that he was disgusting and out of order. "You should honor thy father and mother. Listen to how you tawk."

He was dismissed as an old lady fag the first day. I tried to assure him they were not always this obnoxious.

"Why dontcha hit 'em?"

I had considered that alternative in my fantasy life.

"It's against the law."

"You're the teacher; they should respect you."

Marco soon occupied a role in the class. He was the conservative Catholic conscience who had a papal opinion on most current events.

"Birth control is a racist plot. God provides."

"You're full of shit, Califano; get a tan and mellow in."

He held his ground.

"I'm saving myself for marriage and I expect my wife to do the same. Lust is for animals."

"Give us a break, Al Bino; girls love it."

"Those are hoores."

"What are you, Master Baiter?"

"That's a moral disorder."

"Have you tried it in a sock?"

"You're a pig. Those base pleasures are contradictory to the teachings of the Church."

The Califanos subscribed to the Catholic Truth Society, publishers to the Holy See.

Marco kept current.

Homosexuality was an abomination to be purged by prayer and abstinence.

"In sacred scripture they are condemned as a serious depravity. Besides, two people of the same sex can't have a baby."

"Not all women want kids, you know, Marco."

"That's the trouble with Americar. Women's Lib makes them feel bad for having a baby."

"You don't think women should have equal rights?"

"Women should be made queens like the Holy Mother."

"You're a mother . . . fucker."

"Don't tawk filth."

"I'll say what I want; it's a free country."

"That's the trouble; it's too free."

Marco found contemporary society distressing. Everything was out of order and too loose.

"The trouble with these guys is they're a godless group."

He'd made an accurate diagnosis there. The majority of kids in that class hated church, found religion boring and

Sundays wrecked if they were dragged to a service of any denomination.

Not so Marco. He was already an altar boy, doing three masses a week. The kids nicknamed him the Bleached Priest.

"I ain't gonna be a priest. I want to be married, but none of this crazy stuff like Californier."

"We'll get you a New York powder puff who hates the beach."

"I mean it. To me marriage is forever, not just some cheap shot in the dark like here."

"I want lots of lovers like Bianca Jagger has."

"Whaddya crazy? She's a floozy type. You're a nice girl, don't talk cheap."

Marco had old-world values that would charm the socks off the nearest grandmother.

He stood up when a female entered the room.

He never left without saying good-bye.

Please and thank you were automatic words, uttered without self-consciousness.

He was groomed to perfection, right down to the after-shave he used on his hairless cheeks. He opened doors for girls, then waited to go in after them.

I never heard him use a cussword. He believed in right and wrong, and those who drowned in gray were spineless. Marco thought the key to a happy life was to live it by the rules.

"Look, it's easy. The guy is the headahouse, his wife is the honored guest, the kids behave, and they all love God."

Since a vast percentage of his classmates came from

divorced homes or creatively arranged living conditions, few gave Marco any credence.

"Snowdrift, your theory's fucked."

"Don't curse."

"You get a date yet?"

"My social life is nonna your business."

"I guess that means no."

We were slogging through contemporary issues to learn about current events and form an opinion. Marco had a tableau of stands that he freely offered.

Giving back the Panama Canal was treasonous to vets.

The Women's Conference in Houston was an insult to all good men around the world.

Nixon was framed.

Billy Graham made too much money.

The Pope should bless Laetrile.

Women can't be priests, and priests need to be celibate to be close to God.

Anita Bryant was correct, but too vicious.

America should be less chicken with the Soviets.

Margaret Trudeau should be ashamed of herself.

The class jeered and booed his right-wing positions.

He remained unmoved. "These are the kinda bums who vote for abortion and stand in welfare lines."

I failed to make the connection in the realm of the reasonable.

"See, it's hard for you to understand."

He stood up straight and smoothed his shirt. "Don't take this wrong, okay?"

He lowered his voice so the vultures circling nearby could only guess the content. "You're very nice, but you're too liberal."

I thanked him for that insight.

Mrs. Pines blinked in to make a spot-check on Marco. She wanted to see him for some meaningful conversation. I signaled him to come forward, which he did with minimal enthusiasm.

Meanwhile, Mrs. Pines puffed out a question to me. "I've been reading a great deal of Krishnamurti, have you?"

She smiled and tsk-tsk'd when I said no.

She whisked Marco off to a bench outside, where they could speak in open space.

He wandered back in, bewildered.

"That lady's a dingbat. Why do I need to be Rolfed?"

"What?"

"She said it would free me up. Free, free, everything's free in Californier, free love, free ride, free spirit. Buncha garbage."

I gave him a hug and he blushed.

"Every dame in this state don't play widda full deck."

He raced to his seat lest I do it again.

The class passed from discussions of police brutality and the needless busts for marijuana, to the issue of the legalization of the devil weed itself. Legalization won a majority vote of thirty-one for, one against.

"Foist of all it's against the law, so poison the bums with paraquat. They should drop dead, not cough."

"Oh eat shit, Califano, you don't know what you're saying. Do you ever get high?"

"My body is the temple of the Lord."

"So God gets off too?"

"Don't say nuttin' against God."

"Fuck you, Marco Narco."

"I ain't castin' my poils to swine. This place stinks. I want to be back in Jersey where people make sense!"

"Then fuck off home, white fright."

"I don't need your garbage. You'll all be in hell."

"Right, paleface, we'll be burnin' in the Devil's Disco Inferno."

"That's another thing, the dancing here is dirty. What about cheek to cheek, where it's slow and nice."

Harvey Flannigan and Mike Shiller stood up and rubbed rear ends in an obscene variation on the bump.

"Cheek to cheek, snowball. *Slow and nice.*"

There was one time Marco got the last word.

On a foggy night in March, Mr. Gordon, a beloved vice-principal, was hit head-on by a semi while coming home from a meeting. We were told one by one as we picked up our mail the next morning. Teachers sobbed openly in the workroom. The principal decided it would be better to dispel rumors by telling the kids at once.

We met on the grass. I remember the damp, heavy air and the feel of the dew on the lawn.

Mr. Kessler told them gently: "We are like a family here, and as head of that family I have some sad news to share."

He worded it carefully, making sure they knew what happened.

Many kids cried out loud. One little girl threw up. The boys tried to choke off public tears, but few succeeded. Mrs. Pines squinted and sighed at the children. A hush fell over the crowd. The air was thick with sadness.

That was when little pale Marco Califano inched his way to the microphone. He said good morning to Mr. Kessler and stepped forward and made up a prayer:

Make a joyous sound unto the Lord
Be happy and satisfied you were given
dominion over animals and plants.
You are worth so much more than these.
Don't offend His everlasting grace
for it is always present
supporting and warming the heart
when it is lost.
The Lord will take care
of Mr. Gordon
of that I am sure
otherwise it makes no sense.
God Bless Mr. Gordon
and God Bless us
even if it is Californier.

Amen

Mother and Child

It was during a midterm exam in Mr. McConnley's Geometry I class twenty years ago that Linda Shillmaker slid me a note.

"Did you hear that Bonnie Walkers and Butch Kramer are getting married? She's pregnant. Don't tell anyone."

I can vividly recall feeling furious with Linda for saying such a thing.

Bonnie was a straight-A student, a cheerleader, a "nice girl."

And she was only fifteen.

Butch Kramer was the starting quarterback for the varsity football team. He'd been offered a full ride at several universities.

My shock was so profound that I talked to my mother about it. She reassured me that these things happen, but since it was Bonnie, it was probably gossip.

I started to scrutinize Bonnie in P. E. Her stomach was flat;

she didn't look like a girl "in trouble." The gold football that hung from her neck merely meant she was going steady, a condition most of us coveted.

A month later I saw her crying in the library by the Periodical Index. Her blond-streaked bubble hairdo shook with the motion of the miserable. She had a checkout form in her hand.

"Why are you leaving, Bonnie?"

I had to hear it from her, cruel as it sounds now. I couldn't help myself. I wanted her to tell me she was getting married.

"It's personal."

The following year, while we crammed for the Constitution test and organized the prom, Bonnie took care of her baby daughter and took a course at night school toward her diploma. Butch boxed groceries at Big Bear and played ball with his buddies on the weekend.

I was afraid to go visit her, scared that my unencumbered life would make her feel bad or me feel bad or whatever. I never clarified those emotions.

Bonnie's situation made me guiltily uncomfortable. I didn't understand how she could *let* it happen.

I had never had intercourse and did not fully comprehend the dynamics of "getting carried away."

I knew boys had rubbers in their wallets. My mother called them "safes."

I had heard stories about Seven-Up douches though no one ever verified if they were real.

I knew Bonnie had ruined her life. Somehow it was supposed to be her fault.

Today is supposed to be different.

Today teenagers are supposed to receive real information about their bodies; we say they are entitled to know about the Pill, the coil, the diaphragm, foam, condoms, jellies, and creams.

Kids today can be tested for pregnancy or V. D. in confidential privacy.

A girl who chooses may have an abortion without parental consent. In some enlightened communities she is no longer kicked out of school if she opts to have the child. But this is still not the norm. The educational reasoning behind the removal of a pregnant girl is so "she won't give others ideas." Some district administrators go even further. Among the more memorable statements I have heard:

"She should think more of herself than to stay."

"Her presence upsets the others."

"It's unhealthy."

"She should have more respect for the boys."

"I would make my daughter hide her shame."

"She'll have to drop P. E."

"If they don't see it, they won't do it."

The facile and obvious answer is not to get pregnant in the first place. It seems ironic that despite all the availability of information and the means of contraception, unwanted pregnancy is still an agonizing adolescent problem.

In a society still hostile to sexual activity outside of marriage, it just may be easier to get caught in an act of spontaneity than to prepare for the clearly established "fact" that one is sexually active.

My students confirm this year after year.

"To be on the Pill means you do it, which means you're a slut unless you're going with the guy."

The rewards for responsibility are few.

"My mother found my pills and I'm on restriction for the rest of the year. My dad cried."

"My boyfriend doesn't want me to take them cuz he thinks they're dangerous, but I think he's afraid I'll sleep with others."

"Once it was known that I was on the Pill, I got a reputation as an easy lay."

"I don't take them because I don't want to gain weight."

Many upsetting tales of physicians' reactions to young girls' requests for contraception have circulated among counselors and health educators.

"I have to ask your mother."

"Someday you'll want to marry; perhaps you should think about this."

"Boys take a dim view of easy girls."

"Stick to petting."

"Save yourself."

"You're not married, so the answer is no."

In the last eight years of teaching, approximately five girls a month have confided in me that they are "in trouble." No two situations have been alike, save the lack of prior planning. Each of my female colleagues reports a steadily increasing number of girls who sobbingly confess to them that "I only did it once and I am frightened."

In truth, they are terrified.

After considerable turmoil, the majority of girls with whom I have had contact chose a quick, therapeutic abortion. I have known only a few who left town and put the baby up for adoption. It is more frequent that a young girl who goes to term with her pregnancy will keep the baby. More often than not, the girl's mother grudgingly raises another child. Few schools provide day-care facilities for children of students.

Only once was I privy to the oddest of love stories, a teenage pregnancy that was strangely joyous, touching in its singularity.

Her name was Heather, and as the word implies she was Scottish-meadow lovely, reed-thin, and fragile. Her porcelain skin glowed in the fall sunshine of the Santa Ana September. Although she was a newly arrived freshman, her presence was immediately remarked by everyone.

There was a section on campus, referred to as Independent Study Corner, that was habitually peopled by jocks and socialites. One had to walk by it in order to get to the library. When Heather passed, all eyes were on her.

The football team gave her an unconditional ten.

The girls acknowledged her beauty, but labeled her a snob.

Actually she was painfully shy, a borderline agoraphobic. She retreated to her house as soon as school was out and would not leave until the next morning.

Heather's parents were divorced, and she and her older brother, Luke, lived with their mother. Mrs. Brockton sold Avon products by day and recited novenas at night for the lapsed Catholics of the world. She was a member of the

Legion of Mary and the local Catholic Women's Prayer Group and the president of the Ladies' Auxiliary of the local parish.

Her own children rarely saw her. When she was home, they did not converse except when Mrs. Brockton had some criticisms to voice about the functioning of the household. Heather did all the cooking and cleaning. Luke did the shopping, since the Mayfair grocery store didn't frighten him. Mrs. Brockton would come home promptly at six to a hot meal on the table. She conducted grace.

Heather's talent for school was considerable. She did not talk or participate, but her assignments were done punctually and with excellence. Her math teacher praised her capacity to catch on. Her science lab write-ups were so impressive that her teacher toted them to conferences. She played the piano for Girls' Chorus.

I looked forward to her English papers for their freshness of ideas. She felt the characters in a book instead of explaining them. She saw people's vulnerabilities as sacrosanct terrain where criticism was forbidden.

Boys frightened her. Suffice it to say that most adolescent admonitions of affection are awkwardly offered in the first place. The star quarterback fell at her feet, panting "I've got to have you." The student body president sent her messages in empty milk cartons thrown across the cafeteria in aim of her tray. The first string of Junior Varsity basketball held a contest to see who among them could get a date. Even the campus stud got into the act by offering her his phone number, telling her "I'll make it worth your while."

She recoiled from all of them.

They voted her homecoming princess.

She declined by writing the team captain an articulate thank-you note, ending with a firm, polite no.

She found a friend in November. A tall, skinny, bespectacled intellectual whom the students called the Praying Mantis or Gordon the Geek, depending on mood. They sat next to each other in my class, never speaking except to steal a tender glance.

Gordon was a new student from Virginia. His military father had been transferred to California. Gordon said "sir" and "ma'am," read chemistry books for fun, was an amateur ornithologist who also took pictures of wildflowers with his Nikon.

He had a merciless reception since he was not tan, sportive, hip, or radical.

Heather said yes when he asked her to eat lunch with him. They stationed themselves in the far corner of the freshman lawn, away from the judgmental onlookers.

They were rarely apart from then on. Two Victorian wallflowers hand in hand amid the jeers and vitriol of the social elite, who burst into "All You Need Is Love" if they happened to walk by. I don't think they even noticed.

Kent Peterson found a love note to Heather from Gordon and posted it on the board. He had compared Heather's beauty to the ruby-throated thrush granger, which greatly amused those who'd never heard of this bird.

We were nearing Christmas vacation and spirits were restless. A local radio station came to campus with a special assembly on the history of rock 'n' roll. Kids charged for the gym, but Heather and Gordon stayed behind. He spoke first. "Ma'am, we'd like to talk."

Heather blushed and nodded.

"We need to talk about something and our parents wouldn't understand."

"What's up?"

Heather raised her eyes and whispered an ethereal pronouncement.

"We're going to have a baby." She nodded happily.

I was stunned, but puzzled. "Aren't you both fourteen?"

They smiled and confirmed their age.

"Are you sure?"

"I had a test that said yes."

"What do you plan to do?"

Gordon had evidently thought it through.

"Obviously, we'll have to tell our parents, but not now. Mine would overreact and insist upon an abortion."

Heather cringed at the word.

"I won't do that, because I believe it is murder. I couldn't live knowing I destroyed a part of us. My mother is going to kill me."

"What will you do? I have the names of some very good people who will counsel you."

Gordon thanked me, but they had plans.

"We've devised an exercise program and a nutrition regime

that will keep Heather in shape and healthy until summer, when she delivers."

"Have you seen a doctor?"

"Yes, ma'am. He gave her some vitamins and a list of adoption agencies."

"Heather, do you feel good about these choices?"

She gave me a faraway look. "We made them together. Gordy and I are going to share this experience, since there is no other way for us."

"I don't know how this happened, ma'am. I thought we were careful, considering."

"Considering what?"

Heather started to cry. "Considering it was the most beautiful moment of my life, and I'm not sorry."

Gordon put his arms around her and kissed her head.

"It's going to be fine. We'll nurture it together and see that it gets a good home."

"Then you'll put your baby up for adoption?"

"We will place it in a family, yes."

"Do you need my help?"

"No, ma'am; we just wanted to share our secret with someone."

He walked her to lunch and bought her two cartons of milk. They sat together on the lawn, feeding the birds that gathered in the sun.

I thought about them a lot. He was tender and solicitous; she seemed happy and in good health. Her cheeks were rosy. She kept me posted on her changes.

"Doctor says I'm in great shape. No more morning sickness."

They both got straight A's at midterm.

"My breasts are bigger. Can you tell?"

I really couldn't. She showed no signs of pregnancy by March. She wore her usual school clothes, which still fit.

"I tell smokers to put out their cigarettes. I don't want poison around this baby."

"Heather, how do you pay for the doctor?"

"Gordon has a paper route. I have savings."

"When do you plan on telling your mother?"

"As late as possible. We want to enjoy this while we can."

In April I studied her profile. I could not see a bump or detect a swelling. She assured me it was growing. Heather whispered to me as I passed back exams.

"I felt it move in Biology. It was so lovely."

Gordon kept precise records in a diary he'd started at Christmas. Heather told me he wrote poems to his unborn child. Gordon walked a little ahead of Heather in the halls to see that no one bumped her. He touched her stomach at lunch on their secret spot of grass.

In early May her grades went down.

Her teachers remarked that her concentration had disappeared. She got chastised in Math and cried in class. "How can I listen to his equations when my baby is kicking me?"

She let me feel her belly. Sure enough, there were ferocious jabs against the taut muscles of her abdomen.

"Heather, are you okay? I worry that you're unhappy."

"I'm afraid to tell my mother, but it has to be soon; I'm six months along."

"Will she react badly?"

"She'll want me to keep the baby."

"Seriously?"

"It'll become 'our' baby, and she'll insist that I keep it."

"Are you going to?"

"No. I know it's only mine for a little while. Gordy and I talked about that."

"How does he feel?"

"He tells me he loves it already, but that we're both too young. I think so too."

"Can you give it up, Heather?"

She smiled and felt her belly.

"We've already made our plans. I love both of them enough to give it up."

I didn't question her further.

By late May I could tell, but I knew. The rest of the kids thought she'd put on weight because she was depressed about dating such a clod.

Gordon carried her books, brought her lunch, and walked her to classes. He had a peculiar gait and by now she walked oddly. They were a touching twosome in the halls.

They told their parents on June 1. Gordon's mother went to pieces, shrieking that her son had been trapped by a slut. His father sat clench-jawed, reviewing potential solutions.

Heather's mother cried and then beat her with a broom

handle. Luke interfered. When she calmed down, she talked to Heather about picking out wallpaper for the baby's room. She insisted that Heather be a nursing mother, since natural antibodies are passed on to the infant.

Cautiously, Heather informed her that other arrangements had been made. Papers had been signed. Decisions reached and finalized.

Mrs. Brockton's rage was complete. She pulled her out of school and kept her restricted inside for the summer. Gordon was forbidden to be near her; his parents were threatened with a lawsuit if he tried.

Gordon sulked around campus like a disheartened Romeo. He sat by himself on the patch of grass and mournfully ate Fritos.

He failed most of his finals. His parents suggested military school. He took a job in a florist's shop so he could steal flowers and send them to Heather. He'd smuggle messages in shopping sacks, shoes, tennis ball cans, or library books.

She went into labor late in August. Luke Brockton phoned Gordon from a booth outside the men's room at the hospital. Mrs. Brockton tried to have him removed, but he was the father, even though he broke the children-under-sixteen-not-admitted rule.

Richard Gordon Brockton weighed seven pounds three ounces. Five days later he was placed with a young couple whose joy was only matched by Heather's courage. Gordon went with her.

They know where and with whom Richard resides.

They both feel his life will be happy and they made the right choice.

Heather and Gordon returned in the fall. Mrs. Brockton went back to her prayers and resumed ignoring her daughter. Gordon's parents repressed the whole affair.

Every lunch hour Gordon and Heather could be found nestled on the lawn, away from the groups of kids, alone and holding hands.

The school paper called them the Oddballs. The drill team named them Beauty and the Beast. They called each other "love."

In the yearbook of their senior year, one can find a perfect photo of the two of them. Their schoolmates voted them class couple, which was intended to be an in-joke by the journalism staff.

Heather and Gordon, in black and white, seated primly on the green turf of their consistent rendezvous, both smiling into the camera. They look like any high school couple whose romance flourished throughout the mindless activities of the carefree teenage years.

Dark Shadows

It has been referred to as "the dark secret" and "America's shame"; it has been dramatized by such books as *Somewhere a Child Is Crying.*

There is no nice label for child abuse.

It is a widespread problem that respects no class lines, income brackets, educational levels, ethnic or religious groups.

I once checked with a local hospital as to the number of cases reported per month. I was told "approximately one hundred, but we're under close scrutiny because it's near a military base."

I asked the official whether most doctors reported suspected child abuse.

"I doubt it, since most doctors know nothing will happen."

I asked him to explain.

"I have a girl friend who's a D. A. They haven't prosecuted one case of child abuse this year. There's no time."

"Then what do these children do?"

"Depending on their age, they either run away or get beaten up."

In-service training has begun in the schools to teach teachers to recognize child abuse and take the proper steps.

I saw my first 516 form last year. We learned all the proper terms, the correct channels to go through, the names of agencies, and people to write to, to bring about political pressure for legislation.

We didn't talk about our feelings. Most of us knew more than we would share.

I dream about Diane. Her presence still haunts me.

I cannot forget her eyes, so pained from the death of her mother, with whom she had had a stressful relationship. The lonely droop of her maloccluded mouth, permanently positioned in a semi-sneer.

Diane, sixteen years old, acne-ridden, myopic, overweight, and underachieving in all subjects, including P. E.

Diane, home alone with her unemployed aerospace-engineer father who cursed her existence, spent her Social Security checks, took her baby-sitting money, drank himself into stupors, and demanded that she take care of him.

Her older sisters had fled in self-defense. One joined the navy; the other ran off to New Zealand with a hitchhiker she'd picked up.

Diane, squinting into pages of books she hated through

scratched-up prescription lenses whose effectiveness had waned years before.

She offended her teachers by her ornery attitude; her classmates found her aggressive, uncooperative, aggravating. She bit her nails to the quick and they bled in tiny spurts when she wrote, which was as seldom as possible.

She was placed in a reading class for students who were below grade level. Her test scores implied that her skills were somewhere around fifth grade. According to her records, that was the year her mother became ill.

The first day, she threw a freshman boy across the room, kicked another in the shins, and made it clear to me that "being in this asshole class was not my idea."

If I asked her to come to my desk, she would refuse. She would deliberately put her shoes in her purse, because one strictly enforced rule in California concerns the wearing of protective footwear. Any attempt at making her comply would bring a hail of hostile comments and unsolicited sneers.

Her hair was a tangled oily mess of blond wires jetting off in all directions. She carried herself with the self-conscious slump reserved for young girls who possess premature bustlines. Rarely were her clothes clean and ironed. Hems drooped from neglect, safety pins glistened on bra straps stained from lack of washing.

She worked in the cafeteria, which entitled her to the hot-lunch program. The hair-netted ladies found her impossible to talk to, but she did her job. Behind her back, they chirped about today's permissive society and how hard it must be for her father to raise her alone. Diane scooped and slung mashed potatoes on passing trays, ignoring everyone.

She refused to be tested for vision and hearing. The nurse tried calling home, but her father slammed down the receiver with yelps of "Don't bother me; she's a big girl."

I tried to talk to her about these health checks.

"Diane, these tests are so you can get your license. Don't you want to drive?"

She sulked into her dirty fingernails and wouldn't speak.

"Diane, it's a quick jaunt. All she'll have you do is read a chart and listen for beeps."

She dug her hands into her thighs.

"Tell her to mind her own goddamn business."

"It's not a question of snooping."

"Bullshit. She's always marching around with this phony crap about in your best interest. Tell her to stay the hell out of my life."

She wouldn't budge. I didn't feel that I could insist further, but I did talk to the nurse about it.

"Her math teacher suspects a hearing loss. Apparently she doesn't follow his instructions."

"She's most likely ignoring them."

"He thinks she lip-reads."

I watched Diane more closely. If you spoke behind her, she didn't answer. I said something as she looked intently at the latest copy of *Seventeen*. She raised her head to utter an annoyed "What?"

I repeated the conversation. She watched my lips and formed the words with hers.

The vice-principal had received more complaints about her behavior. She slapped a girl at milk break, threw her books down in a rage during the Ohio Vocational Inventory being given in the library. We were asked to keep records on deportment in class.

A freak accident in P. E. caused the unraveling of the uncomfortable truth about Diane's life. She fell off the balance beam and landed on a mini-tramp. Her teacher feared broken ribs, so the school physician was called. Upon request, he sneaked in an ear check.

Her tympanic membrane had been shattered. According to him, it had probably been caused by a blow of sorts. Her other ear showed previous damage.

The doctor questioned her about her ears. She roared contemptuous obscenities and bellowed at him to stick to ribs.

School doctors are volunteers and expect great gratitude. He left in a fury, vowing to stick to his private practice since he didn't need this kind of headache.

Quite by accident, I found her on the freeway one day shortly afterward, thumbing her way south. I veered off the road, pulling to a dangerous stop, indignant at her carelessness. Just weeks before, a high school girl had been picked up hitchhiking and brutally murdered.

She ran to the car, panting, and jumped in.

"Thank God, you saved my ass. I'm late."

"Diane, you know better than to be hitching on the freeway."

"Gun this mother, for Christ's sake. I'm in a hurry."

"Where are you going in such a rush?"

She directed me to a middle-class neighborhood on winding streets with musicians' names. Left on Liszt, sharp right on Chopin, to the corner of Bach and Vivaldi. She dove to the floor, shaking.

"Drive by here fast. Don't slow down."

I did as she asked, but I saw him in my rearview mirror. He didn't look fierce out there pruning roses. His hair was thin, graying, and he wore baggy green pants like one sees on TV repairmen.

"Let me off around the block. I'll jump when you stop."

"Diane, what is happening here?"

"I gotta go, thanks."

She jumped out to survey the surroundings. Apparently all was clear. I watched her walk home. She rounded the corner and changed her pace to a fast-moving frenzy.

She came to school the next day in a foul humor, coiled and ready to strike any intruders.

She grabbed Ricky Donaldson by the hair and banged his skull into the magazine table.

"You little son of a bitch, grab my book again and I'll crunch your fucking legs."

I pulled her off in a rare moment of courage and strength.

Ricky clenched his fist, but he didn't swing.

I yanked her outside. "Just what in the living hell are you doing?"

I saw the bruises on her neck. Tiny marks the size of mini sand dollars just above the collar bone.

"He took my book, the bastard. I'm going to kill him the next time."

"What happened to your neck, Diane?"

"Nothing."

There were tears stinging in her eyes.

"Did your father hurt you?"

I already knew the answer.

She let out a wounded coyote howl and slumped down on the lawn.

"I'm bad. I try to be good, but I keep doing rotten things."

I reached to touch her, but she brushed my hand away.

"What do you do that's so rotten?"

She looked like a crumpled version of the little Danish mermaid, all huddled over and shaking with sorrow.

"I forget he likes the house dark and his food on time, and he doesn't like me to watch him stare at the picture. He gets mad because he's embarrassed."

"What picture?"

"Of my mom."

"Diane, does he hurt you?"

"He's in pain all the time. I make him mad."

"Can we help you?"

She was on her feet in a second. Tears streamed down her chin.

"Don't tell anyone. Just forget it."

She avoided contact for the next few days, making sure we could not talk.

Her P. E. teacher noticed unusual bruises on her back and buttocks. Diane said she fell down skateboarding.

It was the burn that called us all to attention. She could not explain the burn on her shoulder and upper arm. The nurse called her teachers to a meeting after school.

She sat us in a semicircle, like story time at the children's library.

"Diane Saunders is being abused."

Those words pelted my stomach like shelled peas hitting a pot. Tiny explosions of ugly suspicions being pronounced as ugly facts.

"That is a third-degree burn on her shoulder. Someone did that to her."

Her math teacher shifted uncomfortably, keeping his eyes on the floor. Her P. E. teacher folded her arms.

The vice-principal took a deep breath and stood up. "We have no other choice but to proceed. I'll call the sheriff and Bonwit Receiving. Perhaps we can have her admitted today."

We didn't look at each other.

Diane was taken to the shelter that evening. The sheriff warned her father not to try and keep her when he refused to let her go. They were forced to go in and take her.

According to the report, their house was bleak and dark, all the shades were pulled down and sealed with masking tape. There was scarcely any food except for boxes of Quaker Oats, butter, brown sugar, and beer. Mountains of empty half-quart cans were found in the garage. The credenza by the television set held the pictures. A sad rotogravure of a fractured family. Diane's mother was a wistful-looking woman with intense eyes. One old photo in a gold frame caught the officer's eye. The entire family was seated in a toboggan, like stair steps. Diane was the tiny bottom rung, all bundled up in winter clothes and smiling.

Diane denied any mistreatment, protesting that her father loved her and didn't they know enough to let a sad man alone.

Her father sat passively through all the questions. He had nothing to say to anybody.

A caseworker came to see him.

He threw her out.

Diane ran away from the shelter. She was found sleeping in her own backyard, unknown to her father, who was staring drunkenly at the television screen inside.

She threw a violent tantrum at Bonwit and hurt a young runaway.

She was placed in solitary for her own protection.

She ran away again two days later. The police were unsuccessful in finding her.

The father was questioned. He knew nothing. No one at school had seen her. Her baby-sitting clients were interviewed. No one had a clue.

According to her father and the Bonwit, Diane had no money. No clothes.

Her father sold the house.

The local papers discreetly stayed out of it.

The neighbors had kept a watchful eye on the comings and goings. They had heard the screams for years. No one had ever reported anything, except to each other over coffee and whispers of "Isn't it a shame."

He moved on a Saturday. A truck pulled up and two non-uniformed men hauled away his belongings.

A young couple with two kids moved in within a week. The exterior has been painted a sunny yellow; the roses are in bloom; the fence is repaired.

Only one lead ever came through about Diane.

A young intern in a suburban hospital emergency room treated a girl matching Diane's description for lacerations and a mild concussion. He filed a child abuse form. Evidently the girl was semidelirious, but defensive. She murmured over and over, "You don't understand. I love my father."

He tried to stall her while he summoned the police. She took off when he left the room.

The only witness was a nurse who had just gone off duty. She reported seeing a young girl climb into a car driven by a balding gray-haired man.

High Tea and Crumpets

A confession.

Stuffy, formal, uptight men fascinate me. The tweedy gentleman who insists on propriety, restraint, and politesse captures my bemused attention and inherits a fair share of my sarcasm. I've given up trying to analyze the reason. One thing remains crystal clear: if there's a closet compulsive Victorian nearby, we'll find each other within seconds.

I am always astonished to find amid the blue-jeaned, T-shirted hard rock aficionados an anachronistic throwback to the parlors of polite society. The gentleman—in all the chivalresque connotations of the term—standing out like an Orwellian vision in reverse. Gentry in the jet age.

I had heard about Bradford Billings several times before actually meeting him.

His Social Studies teacher would tell Bradford stories over tuna salad in the cafeteria.

"He refuses to be called Brad; says it's a vulgar diminutive of his proper name."

"Bradford refused to take the state exam because I ran out of number-two pencils."

"Cynthia Epstein asked Bradford to eat lunch with her and he said they hadn't been properly introduced, therefore her invitation must be considered forward and unacceptable."

This was a teacher who liked kids to be kids. For him the pinnacle of high culture was another full six-pack at the bottom of the ninth. If kids didn't exhibit enthusiasm about team sports, student government, and *Star Wars*, they were putting on airs. He would always include a freebee question on his Social Studies exams, like:

The final touchdown was made by ——— (2 pts)

In which case, Bradford would include a note under the blank space protesting the irrelevance of trivia to the Louisiana Purchase.

I must confess Bradford vicariously amused me.

Bradford enrolled in an Honors English program for his senior year. We met at registration.

"Excuse me," he said, waiting for me to finish signing the forms. "Would you kindly give me some information regarding the instructor of this class?"

"I hear she's scintillating."

He was not amused and stood there waiting for a serious response.

"What do you want to know?" I asked.

"Her credentials, literary preferences, and to what degree she takes her professional responsibilities seriously."

"Well, Mr. Billings."

"You may call me Bradford, since this is a public school."

"Very well, Bradford. She has two master's degrees, loves the nineteenth-century novel, Vonnegut, Woody Allen, J. P. Donleavy, Jane Austen, and *Cosmopolitan.* And to take this profession seriously is an admission of mental illness."

He digested this for a moment before commenting.

"I see. Eclectic tastes; however, the other course offerings pander to touchy-feely mockeries of education. Sign me up, please."

He thanked me and went to interrogate the Science Department.

I looked forward to working with the genteel scholar in Hush Puppies.

He arrived well before class, to find a suitable seat. He selected front row left because the lighting was more than adequate. He dusted off the seat, set down his blue backpack, and settled in, remarking that a hard back prolonged one's attention span. He unzipped his backpack and lined up three pencils, a stack of lined paper, a box of Gem paper clips, a miniature sharpener, and a pocket dictionary.

I was suitably impressed, since many of his classmates considered a writing utensil excess baggage.

The bell rang and the students poured in. Bradford surveyed his peers with disdain. The class was small, which made me happy. A sharply competitive math whiz slunk into the seat next to his.

"Hi, Brad; what's this?"

He reached for Bradford's dictionary to flip through the pages. Bradford snatched it away with a terse "Do you mind?" He placed it in exactly the same position as before.

"Kindly call me Bradford. Then consider finding another seat. I don't like to feel crowded."

Robert looked at him unbelievingly, and they began to argue.

I was anxious to start the class, so I intervened.

"Could you two gentlemen resolve your territorial disputes elsewhere? I'd like to get moving."

Bradford sat up straight, took a pencil, prepared to take notes, and launched a contemptuous glance at Robert, who moved.

A slight smile of victory spread over Bradford's stiff upper lip.

I explained the course outline. There were a few groans, sighs, and some questions.

Everyone took notes.

Except Bradford.

When the clock ticked one minute before the bell, Bradford gathered up his materials in the opposite order of placing them. The dictionary, the sharpener, the paper clips, the untouched lined paper, and finally the three pencils were zipped back in his pack.

The ritual was achingly familiar. I'd had years of training being with someone who folded towels in threes, brushed his teeth exactly the same way every morning and evening, and regardless of the house insisted on the same items in the same place as the previous abode. I rather like chaos. Our compromises were always intricate negotiations.

Bradford double-checked to see if things were in order. I spoke without thinking.

"Bradford, you are just like my husband. A place for everything and everything in its place. This is going to be a long year."

"I beg your pardon?"

"Obsessive-compulsive neurosis. Your number in the DSM II is 300.3. Learn it now, you'll save some money when you see a shrink."

He half smirked, half sneered. "I trust your spouse is methodical in his approach to life."

"In everything except his choice of mate."

"I see. You seem to be somewhat organized."

"I never measure when I cook, and I throw in any amount of laundry soap I can grab with my hand."

He winced just like I knew he would. I had some misgivings about this semester. I knew I'd drive him crazy, or vice versa, or both. I wasn't wrong.

I sat down on Bradford's desk one day. He was beside himself.

"Unless you remove yourself, I cannot possibly function."

I gave the desk back. He quickly dusted it off, sat down,

distributed his belongings in their proper spot, and sat at attention.

He had not turned in one assignment. We had words about that.

"Bradford, you have to get these in. You are missing six."

"I am aware of my shortcomings. I do have six neatly completed outlines."

"I need the papers, Bradford. Stop procrastinating."

"I guess I do that a bit."

"I bet you line up all your materials, even note cards, assemble everything, then go complete every other inane task imaginable and never get the first sentence written."

"Precisely."

"That method will get you an F."

"I don't feel compelled to measure my self-worth by grades."

"Yes, but you'd like to go to college?"

"My parents strongly urge that course."

"Are your parents as elegant as you?"

"Actually, they're quite common."

"What is that supposed to imply?"

"That I find my house unimaginative, anti-intellectual, and their tastes vulgarly mundane."

"Jesus. That takes care of them. Please do me a favor and put your discriminating ass in gear so that I can truly appreciate your superior intellectual gifts, *d'accord*?"

He smiled and sniffed a "We'll see."

He was flunking by midterm. He'd done all the readings

and more, contributed greatly to class discussions, but had not turned anything in. I yelled at him after class; he looked down at his ordered desk and informed me that I did not understand.

"I am psychologically incapable of being on time with things."

"Then you'll reap the consequences."

"I need the punishment."

I gave him an A for insight.

Bradford made it through Mythology with little problem. He liked the essay unit because it was precise, to the point, and did not offend his bourgeois sensibilities. Marilyn Droso called him a stuffed shirt. He thanked her.

It was the choice of novels that threw Bradford off. *The Awakening* was dismissed as "sentimental fluff." The girls in the class loved the story and talked about the contemporary equivalent of Edna's restlessness. They felt they had it.

Bradford was impatient with their self-indulgence.

"Edna is a tiresome person with morals that are suspect, not to mention questionable."

"What do you mean by that Victorian, not to mention sexist, crap?" asked Florence Drago, scholar, feminist, politico, and debate team captain.

"I choose to ignore your poor choice of words; however, if you will look closely, you will see Edna virtually threw herself at that fellow, so to speak."

"So what?"

"An utter disregard for propriety and decency."

"Oh, wow."

The girls hissed and booed him. The boys laughed noncommittally. Bradford straightened his John Dean glasses, smoothed his perfectly ironed shirt, stroked his starched khaki slacks, and responded calmly.

"The fact remains that Madame Pontellier behaved like a cheap strumpet, imitating the morals of any common vulgarian."

"You're pathetic."

"I prefer to see myself as restrained, which is more than I can say for Edna. She could have had the decency to wait a decent period of time before lunging into passion."

A tape clicked in my head. Ten years earlier on a beach in Mexico, where my spouse first kissed me "because it was time." That meant the third date, since before that would have been improper. It was after that absurd declaration of prudery that I knew I would marry him.

Meanwhile, Bradford was being slaughtered by the high verbals.

"Go find a nun."

"Where did you come from, Victoria's antechamber?"

I quickly changed the subject. "What do you think of Chopin's constant jabs at social pressures?"

Robert spoke up here. He took pride in beating out Bradford for the quickest, most concisely annoying comment.

"No one can adequately judge the universe without a knowledge of crosscultural comparisons and local color."

Bradford jumped at the occasion to contradict his rival.

"If you had the remotest sense of historical perspective, you'd see how patently nonsensical your argument is."

"And why is that?"

"Those questions did not concern Miss Chopin. We are dealing with ethical issues."

Nate called them both schizoids, his favorite word next to *gonads.*

Bradford took offense. "Judge not, Nate, lest you be judged."

"Since when are you religious, Billings?"

"I'm not. One needn't subscribe to some supernatural dogma like ordinary cretins to have an ethical perspective. I was merely commenting on Nate's lack of manners."

"This entire conversation is a pain in the ass and its participants' swelling egos leave no room for the rest of us."

That worked for two minutes and thirty-five seconds. In desperation I yelled, "Shut up.

"We are having a speaker on Wednesday. Mrs. Olsen's class will be joining us."

Bradford's arm went up. "There are not enough seats. Does that mean I must give up my chair?"

He was genuinely concerned. I assured him he could keep it.

He still did not do his papers. We had another chat in this regard.

"Bradford, why do you set me up to be the heavy?"

"Isn't heavy intended to be an adjective?"

"Stop footnoting me."

"I much prefer proper English."

"Bradford, why are you so lazy?"

"I prefer to see myself as thorough."

"A thoroughly phlegmatic slug."

"You snap quite nastily, don't you?"

"You set me up for it, don't you?"

"I always did fancy women with sharp tongues."

"Bradford, we are taking a standardized test tomorrow. You'd better knock me out with your knowledge, because otherwise 'your college-bound ass is grass,' as the common peasants say."

He had his materials lined up and ready the next morning when I passed out the booklets. Since details make me anxious, I told the class I would skip reading the directions, since they were self-explanatory.

"When I say go, begin."

His hand shot into the air like a periscope.

"Do it like you're supposed to."

"Why?"

"Because you're supposed to read the directions."

I pictured my husband standing over me, hyperventilating as I dumped any old amount of water into the Rice-a-Roni.

I read them at breakneck pace with a Southern accent.

He raised his hand again.

"Don't go fast. Repeat it exactly as you're supposed to."

I read the directions carefully and concisely, ending with the authoritative "Begin."

He sighed and began with a smile.

He scored a perfect 800.

The next day he arrived with a note on tasteful stationery:

Mrs. Martin:

At the earliest possible opportunity, please question your spouse for his opinion on the following topics:

Gum chewing
Books printed on poor-quality paper
People who violate one's personal space
Cooking by intuition
Shoddily made merchandise
Strangers who act as if they are friends
Familiarity by salespeople.

He must have known every answer already, but he'd decided to verify.

"Without excess sentimentality, I find your capacity to make your relationship work quite against the laws of logic."

"Love is like that," I said to Bradford.

He should have gotten an F, but all his exams were A's. We compromised on a C, since he'd already been admitted to Berkeley with honors at entrance.

We had a party in class, ate junk food, and signed yearbooks. My inscription from Bradford read:

> As an autonomous person, I resent and reject social pressure to sign people's yearbooks. Exceptions can be made, however, in special cases.
>
> P. S. Those of us who are capable of making good, right decisions agree that you are a fine educator, however disorganized you appear and in fact are.

The phone rang two years later in the small hours of the morning. I went over my mental obituary notices, all of my relatives, friends, and coworkers. Which one would be dead? I braced myself for tragedy.

"Mrs. Martin, I know this is a most inopportune time to be calling, but after much hard thinking it is entirely possible that I am losing my mind."

Though two years later, the voice, the face, the utter lack of hysteria, were all there. Only slightly altered by the tone of urgency.

"Bradford, where are you?"

"In my dorm. I hate it also. Inadequate ventilation."

"Why do you think you're losing your mind?"

"I cannot study."

"What's new?"

"These feelings of confusion. Things are out of order."

He went on to explain that he felt funny, nothing made sense, he couldn't concentrate, his objectivity was blurred. He hated his roommates; they were "mediocre minds in artificially pressed bodies." He'd become quite fond of a Jewish girl with terse diction, but he was afraid of her. I suggested he get counseling at the Health Center at once.

"I cannot abide losing my dignity to someone who will massage my feet to release psychic trauma."

"What kind of horseshit have you been reading? He'll talk to you, Bradford. He's trained to listen and decode. He has credentials. Go! That's an order. I'm calling you back tomorrow. Don't you *dare* drag your feet here. I mean it; GO! Good night."

I sounded wonderfully ominous, if I do say so. He went.

"Well?"

"It is very nice to hear your voice again."

"Did you go?"

"Yes."

"And?"

"I liked him. He stood up when I came in and asked if he could call me Bradford."

"Yeah?"

"We talked for two hours, for free. He thinks I'm depressed and that's why I'm—he called it 'compulsive.' " Then he laughed. So did I.

"Do I get to say I told you so?"

"Certainly not."

"I'm really delighted you went, Bradford. Will you continue?"

"As long as it's beneficial and practical."

"Right. How's your female friend?"

"She's rather pushy."

"You love her, right?"

"Perhaps. Love is a rather vague term."

"Bradford? I'm glad you're doing whatever you're doing."

"Thank you."

We were disconnected. The buzz of the dial tone was oddly musical.

He kept up therapy.

He quit school to study, explore, and experience. He'll go back.

At present he's interested in birds, Mexican pottery techniques, motorcycles, and straight-sided polygons in tension. I got one card from the Yucatan.

> Interesting terrain. School seems remote; however, I will never choose to remain uneducated. Am traveling with a girl who is most disorganized. Her backpack is a disgraceful mess, not one item folded properly. I may be in love.

I crawled into bed that night wondering what loving a Bradford would be like. My husband came in, pulled the spread back, smoothed the bottom sheet, fluffed his pillow, slid in carefully, turned on his side, and pulled the covers over his left shoulder so they barely touched his neck. He slid his arm around my waist and pulled me to him with a kiss.

"Mellie, the dishwasher is loaded wrong. Those pans go on top. I love you."

You'll do fine, Bradford. Just don't lose your sense of humor.

Huarached Socrates

Cardinal Rule Number One in Introduction to Educational Philosophy is, Never touch a student. This is not a metaphysical message, but a legal edict. The word *touch* is inclusive of several kinds of contact. Violence is out, manhandling strictly forbidden, and any form of physical intimacy is not only shockingly unethical but grounds for immediate dismissal.

Each violation takes place daily.

The horror stories kids relate about elementary school incidents are made worse by their continued secrecy. Tales of humiliation by dictatorial teachers are commonplace. Most kids won't confess to being hit at school for fear of another slap at home.

The subject of love is even more skirted as an issue. In hushed tones, Education professors whisper moral turpitude cases as warnings of ruined lives. The bottom line couches no ambivalence; "keep your distance" is the credo, and there are concrete rules of how you do this:

Mr., Mrs., Miss, or *Ms.* is a good beginning. Knowing your first name breeds a dangerous atmosphere.
Never relate stories about your personal life.
Always keep the door open when you are alone with a student.
Do not accept gifts.
Receive personal compliments with an impersonal "Thank you."
When chaperoning a social occasion, never dance with a student.
Give no one a ride home.
Under no circumstances should your hands rest on a student's body when you are checking his/her work.

Aspiring teachers are asked to memorize these prescriptions for behavior.

They are, of course, unrealistic nonsense. Teachers care about students. Students care about teachers. The classroom is a community where relationships are built and sustained. Sharing and caring are essential components of learning. How do you keep love out of this process?

Quite simply, you don't.

This is not to imply that you act upon these emotions, but

to deny their existence is to belittle their importance. More damage is done by distance than by closeness. Most teachers have quietly loved a pupil.

Dana looked like a thirty-year-old, a peeling Neptune. His scraggly blond hair had not been washed or combed for months. He wore an Army-green gas-station-attendant shirt with four buttons missing and a brightly embroidered *Eddie's* on the pocket. His cutoffs were paint-stained and frayed on the edges, where paisley boxer shorts drooped around like limp ruffles.

He had no concept of punctuality. It became a habit to mark him absent, because he would inevitably sashay in about ten minutes after the bell. He'd staked out the middle seat, last row, against the wall, the first day. Students have a gut understanding of territorial imperative.

He'd sit down slowly and twist his legs into a convoluted yoga position and stare through me for the 110 minutes of Comparative Literature. He never altered his pace. He never talked in class. When the bell rang, he gathered his books and walked out without looking back.

I only knew his name.

Dana Woodrow Benson.

And that his eyes made me uncomfortable. I was constantly aware of his laser-beam leer, especially during lectures.

I hid behind a podium, but it didn't help.

Discourses on Bovaryism were distorted by a desire to

check my stockings for runs. His expression never changed. I tried to decode the look. Extreme boredom? Virulent hostility? Patient pity? Weary tolerance?

His presence made me nervous. When he was absent, I would free up, be spontaneous and more relaxed. Controlled anxiety took over when he returned.

He printed his papers in microscopic prose. He gave only essential information. Adjectives were sparse and carefully chosen. His own opinions were deliberately kept out.

I would circulate around the room to hand back assignments. I avoided his eyes when I returned his. He never said thank you. He never said anything.

He smelled awful. A mixture of stale tobacco and perspiration. His nails were topped in black. A package of Tramp cigarettes popped out of his breast pocket just above *Eddie's.*

Most students hide their cigarettes, since it's illegal to have them.

The staff was assigned the library for their preparation periods since all free rooms were being used for Civil Defense drills.

I was trying to correct essay tests on *Madame Bovary.* The students were to explain why she had opted for suicide. The papers were amusingly hopeless, with an occasional idea worth digesting:

"If Emma was my wife, I'd feed her rat poison just cause she was a drag."

"All men break your heart, so what's the difference if you live or die?"

"She should have had a career."

I smelled him before I saw him. He sat across the table from me, twisted his legs funny, and stared.

"Do you mind if I ask you a question?"

I know I jumped when I didn't want to. His voice was a bizarre blend of Peter Lorre's I'm-going-to-do-terrible-things-to-you tone and Orson Welles's roar as Mr. Rochester.

"No." I was aware that my voice had gone up seven octaves. The odor was pungent by now. I put my wrist under my nose to catch faint whiffs of Je Reviens.

"I've been thinking some."

I was reassured, temporarily.

"Don't you see Emma as the embodiment of the mind/heart dichotomy?"

My answer was nervously unabridged.

"What?"

"The heart does not discriminate in its allotting pleasure. The mind picks and chooses what would be well accepted by the thinking others. The heart takes only what would be accepted by feeling others. If freedom is the ability to negate possibilities, then the heart is not free; it is a plenum of hearts."

I did not know what *plenum* meant, and I could not get my mind to stop contemplating why he didn't bathe. He thought I was evaluating his words, and waited patiently for my response.

"Exactly what do you mean by that?" I was doing my best under the circumstances. He didn't change expression.

"I mean that Emma is framed by the reader's patronizing think judgments. Consciousness is the first moment of self-consciousness." I mulled that over for a minute.

"You're saying we rob Emma of her feelings because we try and label them?"

"In a sense. I've always wished Karl Marx had taken a little trip to Dublin to meet Leopold Bloom."

"What's the relevance?" I asked, resorting to my existential banter of graduate school. He didn't flinch.

"Question. Name the son of a philosopher. We are expected to accept the words of the philosopher. But we cannot know his philosophy as the son knows. The son is the word for all, not simply the thought. Will we be saved by the son? No. What would the son know of the father? A man with constipation of the heart."

I really did try to follow his logic, but I was justifiably perplexed. Nobody talks like this on a high school campus. Well-educated historians and physicists speak of Tupperware and real estate holdings. The Ph.D. from Harvard who heads the Math Department sells Amway products to coworkers during lunch. The counselors are into antique cars, and Home Ec is obsessed with food additives. I've heard the batting average of every Padre, an explanation of why George Allen is a great American, and a rundown on the story line of *General Hospital* since 1963.

"Did you understand what I'm proposing?"

"What grade are you in?" An inane rejoinder.

"Relevance?"

"Touché. I'm just amazed at the level of your analysis."

"Do you always underestimate your students to such a degree?"

"I don't hear that kind of reasoning very often, if that's what you mean."

"Then perhaps you should listen more."

"Perhaps."

I hated him at that instant. There are free-floating forms of criticism that can be looked at, but those who take aim make me defensive and slightly nasty.

"Is this your way of telling me that many a mute inglorious Milton blah blah blah? . . ."

He caught it, God damn him. "I'm just suggesting that some of us are more familiar with our angst than you would care to acknowledge."

"Are you claiming a monopoly on suffering?"

He stared a cold reply and got up.

"I'm the second best thing to Bud Anderson."

I tried to red-pencil remarks about Emma's death. His odor lingered around the table like an invisible sulphuric cloud. I graded the rest without reading them.

He didn't talk at all for three weeks. We'd buried Emma and moved on to the *Odyssey.* Homer appeals to avid Saturday morning television watchers. They accept the heroic events as a matter of course, since all feats of supernatural proportions have already been performed on a video screen by the Roadrunner, the Incredible Hulk, and Wonder Woman.

Dana sat and ruminated in his full lotus. He still hadn't

washed. He made me feel silly for clinging to such bourgeois virtues as soap and water. I kept on trying to ignore his vituperative eyes sizzling in the back of the room.

The kids thought Odysseus's tests of Penelope's loyalty were clever. The girls were glad she had suitors, because it would make her husband jealous. Everyone fantasized what would take place in the olive-tree bed later on.

Dana remained in his seat. Both his feet remained perfectly still on his knees.

His voice resounded from the back of the room.

"Love," he echoed, "announces itself with a swelling of sorts, then a real wave of despair."

"Are you talking about the reunion of Penelope and Odysseus?"

"I'm saying that it's possible to see the loved one's face as the most depthless and infantile image, period."

The bell rang and the room emptied. He stayed.

"That sounds sad. Crazy but sad."

"It's neither. It's meaningless. At least crazy is something."

"Do you ever get tired of your reflective closet?"

"I'm always tired of my cosmitidal moans. Do you care if I smoke?"

I should have said yes, but I said no. We were alone. He lit up a Tramp. He saw that I noticed his brand. I couldn't resist a remark.

"Aren't those a bit trendy for you?"

"You want one?"

"Why not?"

I closed the door. We smoked in a silence that made me nervous, so I broke it.

"How come you know so much about philosophy?"

"I spend a lot of time in bed."

I didn't know how I was supposed to interpret that remark, so I took a puff of the Tramp.

"What are you doing here?" he asked me, fully aware of my avoidance.

"Earning a living, and not a very good one."

"Your face is comfortably alienating."

"Thank you."

"Social amenities are designed to separate people."

"We're supposed to be separated. Why do you have such an aversion to being clean?"

I figured it was an existential trade-off. My face alienates him comfortably. His body odor makes me uncomfortable. When I saw his face, I was instantly sorry.

"It's hard to control things sometimes, but I get by."

He got up and walked out without a good-bye.

Guilt has always been a preferred emotion of mine. When bad feelings settle in like morning fog, I can invent reasons why I deserve them.

Here I knew why.

I entertained the idea of apologizing. He'd probably reject it as insincere formality, but my mood was definitely overcast.

I looked up his records in search of a phone number. I scanned his school photographs from first grade up. He had been an adorable child, blond and smiling. I probed on, forgetting my original purpose. There was no record of second grade. I read further. The teachers' comments were similar, bright inquisitive, cooperative resourceful. Each grade card ended with the same message. Sit him close to the door and let him leave when necessary.

My curiosity peaked. I rummaged through every note, every test score and information sheet for clues. I found a letter from the Mayo Clinic. I read it through twice. The stationery was formal, engraved with impressive names and strings of degrees, letters, Greek symbols, and logos. It was addressed to his third grade teacher:

> Dana is something of a miracle child. The information contained herein is essential to his well-being and should be treated with utmost confidentiality. Dana had a rare form of infant prostate cancer, diagnosed as severely malignant at age 4. After much painful deliberation, his parents consented to experimental surgery and radial cobalt in an effort to prolong his life. The prostate and bladder were removed. His ureters have been joined to his sigmoid colon, and radiation followed. He is being trained to control his sphincter muscles for both urination and bowel function.
>
> To date, he is our longest surviving patient.
>
> Please allow him to deal accordingly and be free to leave the class or lie down when necessary.
>
> Sincerely,
> Ethan Rosemond, M.D.
> Mayo Clinic

I dreamed about him that night. My subconscious tried to fill in gaps and explain things.

I sought him out the next day. He was alone in the quad, staring at pigeons.

"That was a rude remark I made yesterday. I'm sorry, Dana."

"You're saying that because you know the truth, right? Where is it written, in the nurse's files?"

"No, it's in your records. I was looking for your phone number to call you and apologize."

"Bullshit. Well, now you know. Spare me the compassion mode; now you'll never be real to me again."

"Why?"

"Because this always gets in the way."

"Who's underestimating whom?"

"Look, only intellectuals stay in positions they do not feel for, because they can find reasons to stay in authentically."

"What in hell is that supposed to mean?"

"That they can project vividly all the possible dangers of a radical change, to the point where the little emotional discomfort soon becomes a blessing of comfort."

"You mean me? The rest of us just feel pity for you and swim in it?"

"Not everybody, I guess."

I sat down next to him and we were silent for a while. He broke it this time, with the first smile I'd seen from him.

"Any relevant questions?"

I asked a barrage of them, and he gave me straight answers.

Toilet training was torture.

Cobalt had made him sterile and impotent.

He dates often, and it's not a problem as long as he can explain before it becomes one. And yes, he loves sex. He offered that one. And then he told me how.

I was very moved.

He loved the role of giver, and from his description of love, he understood what that meant.

"I can laugh from the depths. I suppose in that sense I'm free."

"Why?"

"Because I'm the only one not projecting irrelevant possibilities past the humor in the moment."

It was precisely at this moment that I fell in love with him.

"Are you up for a surrealistic experience?"

"Yes."

"Come with me to Orange County tomorrow. I hate to drive alone."

I went straight to the office and arranged for a substitute for the next day. I put down root canal as the reason. I didn't see the irony until later.

We met at Speedee Mart, by the ice machine. He was groomed and scrubbed to the point of camouflage. He drove a beat-up Volvo with no muffler.

"Where are we going, Dana?"

"You didn't ask before you chose, so why now?"

"Fair enough."

We made up stories about Lenin and Dedalus as roommates at the London School of Economics. We laughed from the depths.

He turned into a big building off the Jubilee exit.

"Okay, you're my wife and we're both curious."

"Right. I'm Mrs. Benson and I have questions."

Dr. Armillo was a specialist's specialist. He concentrated on reconstructive surgery and innovative ideas. I did not know what was going on until he got specific.

"Mr. Benson, you're obviously adapted to the way you are, and I see your wife doesn't look unhappy."

I smiled and looked happy, but I still didn't get it.

"I've devised a splint implant that is easily inserted under general anesthetic, which will allow you to sustain normal relations."

Dana asked questions. I listened, hoping that my ashen face wouldn't give me away. The doctor continued.

"Why, I did a seventy-year-old last year and I hear he's the terror of Newport. It never goes soft. You just have to learn to package it differently, so to speak."

The supersplint cost two thousand dollars, plus hospitalization. Dana thanked him, and I smiled and shook.

We went to a fashionable restaurant for lunch.

"What was that all about?" I couldn't stop laughing.

"That is the antithesis of the plenum of hearts. It's the plastic of hard-ons."

We held hands like children, which one of us was.

If the mind thinks enough, it will be left with itself, the moment it cuts itself *from* the moment.

I still hear from him after five years. He has been in love four times: a neurotic actress with mood swings, a Jewish Marxist health nut from Brooklyn, a tennis player with my name, and a Seventh Day Adventist social worker who cheats on her beliefs.

He has a degree in philosophy, a job in construction, an interest in film making, and a plenum of hearts that are questing, and will be, hopefully, forever.

❦ ❦ ❦

Showdown at the Karamazov Corral

Simplify, simplify.

Thoreau never taught literature to Sunkist teenagers when the weather was eighty-five degrees, the water seventy degrees, with swells up to six feet and rising.

The "now" generation is impatient. Trying to explain complex ideas to them in contemporary terms often turns into an absurd fiasco.

The boutique journalism approach to learning is so widespread that students retain some interesting facts about the famous, if very little else:

> Elizabeth I was bald.
> Louis XIV died of syphilis.
> James Joyce wrote dirty letters to his wife.
> Proust was gay.

> Dostoyevsky suffered epileptic fits.
> Da Vinci wrote backwards.
> Poe was a doper.

It's like the *Pickwick Papers* according to *People* magazine. I think back upon the aloof professors who would sniff with disdain and inform us that "the work of art or the text itself is the only basis of judgment."

They would then pause for emphasis and scan the rows of intimidated faces for the final pronouncement.

"The rest is none of your business."

The holistic approach to education has encouraged the cult of the personal. The classroom is a community where one shares and grows. Teachers have become facilitators of body/ mind experiences.

One year remains particularly memorable as a mini-version of All in the Extended Family. Consider the cast of characters, all of whom were recruited from the registrar's calculator as the cream of the crop according to grade-point-average computations to the nearest hundredth.

There was Scot, an agile calculus genius who called his math teacher Dad, begged for more homework, and amused his peers by doing tongue push-ups against the blackboard. He also did curls with a ten-pound weight attached to twine. In fits of impulse he'd spring from his seat for one-arm push-ups while he accompanied himself with the tune from *Rocky.*

There was also Bettina, fancied poetess of the spiritual awakening she saw around her between regular bouts of mononucleosis. She sat next to Roland, the class conservative, who kept watch over the socialist scourge he felt was overtaking education in America.

Arnold, the amateur photographer, who wore his camera like a secondary sex characteristic, recorded our madness on film when he wasn't hustling Lori, a redheaded dynamo who wanted to be a space historian, orbiting around in a capsule taking notes.

There was Annie, whose participation in class corresponded directly to the amount of Lithium her shrink was misprescribing at the moment. She was diagnosed a manic-depressive after running away with the manager of an Arco station in a flurry of infatuation that lasted six hours.

And Victor, the acne-riddled Trekkie who wore "I'm with Stupid" T-shirts and had memorized every Spockian witticism since the show's inception. He was secretly in love with Donna, the fashion-conscious cheerleader whose Jewishness was underplayed by her socialite mother, who'd changed their name to Smith after her divorce. She loved Daniel, the scholar-athlete who found God on the five-yard line and spent his time pumping iron and witnessing door to door.

There was Maria, brightest girl in the school, who wanted to be the next Barbara Jordan, whom she admired for her courage and capacity to achieve despite a weight problem.

And David, physics whiz kid, son of a Cal Tech father who urged him on to a Nobel prize, whose own aim was to dazzle crowds in sequined jeans, play like Led Zeppelin, and screw groupies.

And Sam, the mad Texan, crazy for mythology, war games, and racing bikes. He never rested; at all times one of his hyperactive appendages moved, shook, jived, or jumped, waiting for the chance to challenge an assumption. Kathy Carrato, the class housemother—even-tempered, sensible, in tune with others' feelings, in touch with her own—tried to keep him calm, to no avail. Sam called her Marsh-a-mellow.

There was Carl, unwanted son of a Greek immigrant father who cursed his son's piano lessons as "a waste of my hard-earned money on a buncha fag nothin'." Carl retreated quietly to his world of preludes, mazurkas, and nocturnes; the torrent of his father's abuse was finally offset by a scholarship to Juilliard.

Christy Donerly, scientific *Wunderkind*, model, gourmet cook, and swimmer, sat next to Dora, the multilingual cancerphobic, whose family members dressed up in the costume of the country from which her mother had copied the recipe for their weekly international dinners. We looked forward to Thursdays with the curiosity of tourists at the United Nations. Our culinary vocabularies were expanded to include couscous, pumpkin soup, tabouli, and laham maa curry.

Valerie, the vegetarian gospel singer, cringed when Dora described the cuts of meat in each dish. Valerie ran the 440, raised organic vegetables in the backyard, and sang her heart out on Sundays and Wednesday evenings when she'd bring her music to the convalescent hospitals. The pure mellifluous tones of Valerie's version of "He Walks With Me" would give an atheist second thoughts.

Katya didn't sing, but she gave speeches to any group who would listen. Her favorite topics were mercy killing, deaths on the highway, and the importance of dental floss in oral hygiene. She worried that Scot would break his front teeth on the board during a tongue push-up and have to undergo root canal treatments, which, according to her, caused permanent gum inflammation.

Katya annoyed Tim to the point of distraction, but Tim's chivalrous personality would not allow him the luxury of a rebuke. Not so Larry, Varsity wrestler, who sincerely believed that Mexicans had an extra vertebra and therefore didn't mind picking vegetables all day. His personal concept of biological determinism also covered blacks; they smelled different and had smaller brains, not to mention women, whose monthly loss of body fluid prevented them from being successful in business and performing acts of bravery. He told Sonia Finley to check her daily Spanish quizzes for a month if she didn't believe him. Sonia told him to get hosed, which he pointed out was metaphorically symbolic of penis envy. Larry regularly told Katya to close her yap before he whipped a sleeper hold on her.

She interpreted that as a proposition. Everyone laughed except the brothers, Mike and Milton Johnston, quiet scholars of stone-faced seriousness. Mike was a year younger than Milton but he'd skipped a grade, so they were together in all the honors classes.

It wasn't the silence of the two that was so disquieting; it was the utter lack of animation on their faces. Four sharply focused eyes stared ahead, seemingly without blinking. Mike and Milton sat in the middle of the room, trigonometry books on the floor, tiny calculators attached to their belts, Adidas-covered feet pointing toward the front. Both had monotone voices, the pitch and volume always modulated when they spoke, which was rarely. When asked a direct question, regardless of subject, a monosyllabic grunt of yes or no was the answer. Even their handwriting was stiff, vertical printing with tiny dots on the i's and straight lines to cross the t's. Their analytical reasoning followed logical and precise lines of thought with no extraneous adjectives. Penelope was *loyal,* Odysseus *brave*, Telemachus *helpful*, the dog *insightful.*

Quite soon into the semester they became known as Roger and Richard Repressed, nicknames they seemed to find somewhat amusing, which meant their eyes flickered ever so slightly at the mention.

Teaching poetry to this group was torturous. They railed and complained about every poet, demanding why "they couldn't talk English like everybody else."

Digging through *The Rape of the Lock* took three weeks longer than expected, with endless groans stemming from restless boredom.

Bettina thought we should read Rod McKuen.

Victor figured Pope could qualify as a Vulcan, because his emotions were under control.

Donna, the cheerleader, took offense at Pope's tone.

"Personally, I like the trembling rites of pride."

"You would," smirked Sam, tapping out the beat to "Get off My Cloud" on his desk.

Sonia told him to "stick it in his ear."

"There you go again, phallic, phallic." That was Larry, dying to pick a fight.

"Hold it!" shrieked Scot. "I forgot I'm up to fifteen pounds on my curls. *Regardez.*"

He flipped out his twiny lariat, bearing a new weight at the bottom. Out came his tongue, just pointed at the tip and raised slightly. He slid the rope over, making sure the ends were even. Ten curls later, the class was counting, Scot did his finale of a flashing upsweep flip, catching the airborne equipment with his right baby finger. The kids cheered, except for the immobile brothers, Mike and Milton.

I slouched through the Romantics, pulling sentiment out like impacted teeth from these hard-hearted modernists.

"If some guy talked to me about the lily maid of Astolat, I'd puke or dump him."

"If you have to count the ways you love somebody, then it's not love."

"I wish some guy'd call me his duchess."

"This class is boring."

I tugged them along through Arnold and the Rossettis, dipped back to Shelley, Wordsworth, Coleridge, and Keats. The class moaned and squawked. Everyone but the brothers, who took their stoic notes.

I prayed for better reaction to The Novel. Christy wanted to do *The Double Helix*, Valerie suggested *Mine Eyes Have Seen the Glory.* David winged and offered Janis Joplin's biography as a substitute, which was countered by Roland, who thought *None Dare Call It Treason* would greatly benefit the group.

They got stuck with *Crime and Punishment.* The length of the book was the first complaint. Roland thought it was interesting that I'd picked a Russian. Scot vaulted from his chair to press his tongue against the board to build up for the trek into Siberia.

I told them why Freud read and reread Dostoyevsky to probe his character studies.

I suggested they keep a dream notebook and use it as a barometer of what was happening in their waking life. We talked about the function of daydreams, fantasies, and sleeping visions.

Explaining the unconscious to semisomnambulent adolescents is somewhat of a masochistic challenge.

I asked for volunteers to share a dream and connect it to reality. Sam spoke up spontaneously. "I fucked Sonia on the football field while David played some tunes from *The Song Remains the Same*."

At first the class was horrified at such a crude admission. Except for the brothers, who listened without emotion. Sonia smiled and told me later that zapping Sam in his unconscious made her feel victorious because he ignored her in reality.

After Sam's confession, the class became resistant. No one was willing to risk being vulnerable.

"You tell us one of your dreams. Why do we always have to be on the line?"

It was Carl, the introspective musician, who rarely offered an opinion. I was taken aback by his novel boldness.

"Don't you ever dream about us?" he persisted.

"Yes."

"Then you describe one."

My meek "Okay" betrayed my uneasiness. The rest of the

chorus signaled their approval, except the brothers, immobile in their glacial galaxy.

My troubled sleep danced with visions of them.

"Since most dreams deal with violence or sexual fantasy, I'll tell you about the former. I dreamed about the Johnston brothers."

The class tittered and turned to stare at Mike and Milton to gauge reactions. There were none.

"In my dream, both of you were at Los Angeles International Airport waiting in the Pan Am terminal for the next flight to Rome."

"Were you going to visit the Vatican?"

"No."

"Why Pan Am?"

"Let her finish, asshole."

"For some reason I felt ill at ease and looked up from the magazine I was reading. Mike pulled out a gun and started shooting people. I tried to stop him, but he didn't listen. Before we knew it, Milton flashed a Saturday night special and sniped at random."

"What does snipe mean?"

"Picking people off, stupid."

"What were they wearing?"

"Who cares?"

"What happened?"

"I tried every bit of reasoning I could, but neither would stop. Milton grabbed a man and blew his brains out from the temple, exactly like a photo I saw of a Vietnamese being assassinated by an American soldier. I woke up."

"You mean you didn't fuck 'em?"

"Shut up, jerkoff."

"No, I didn't. This was a dream of helplessness and fear."

"Are you afraid of those geeks?"

"I'll kick their ass for you if you want."

"Trig types are killers. I knew it."

"What's the fear?"

Mike and Milton looked ahead, expressionless yet interested.

I asked them what they thought it meant. Mike responded first in a calm and even tone. "It sounds as if you see violence beneath the surface of what you call acting repressed."

I smiled at his insight. Indeed I must have thought of them as raging sociopaths in the recesses of my subconscious.

Milton had a few words. "I interpret it as a lack of control you apparently feel over us."

Another bull's-eye. Not only lack of control, but lack of influence. The discussion quickly deteriorated to hijackings, kidnappings, and other acts of terror.

Sam told the class how to make the perfect bomb at home in the garage. Evidently plutonium is not an impossible commodity to rip off.

I tried to veer the dialogue back to Dostoyevsky, but they weren't interested in Raskolnikov that day.

I couldn't wait to finish the book and get on with the contemporary novel.

I let the class vote on a selection, and *One Flew Over the Cuckoo's Nest* won by a landslide. Apparently they'd all seen the movie.

The boys adored McMurphy and took any opportunity to imitate him. Scot dedicated his new stunt, a headstand push-up, to Kesey's hero.

I had one hell of a time keeping order, especially one day when everyone was fighting over Billy Bibbit's sexual initiation. The girls attacked McMurphy's insensitivity, while the majority of the boys applauded his daring.

I screamed at all of them to sit down and shut up.

Slowly and methodically, Mike and Milton rose to stand.

I saw the silver slip from Milton's pocket first. Mike moved backward toward the door and drew a pistol.

"Don't anybody move!" It was a shattering command that stunned me into breathless inertia.

Sam moved with a hostile hoist and the firing began. Loud pops and cracks filled the air with a smoky fierceness. I watched them fall with detached horror. Valerie, Dora, Daniel, and Scot slumped into heaps of dead flesh on the polished floor. Maria fell forward; I saw the blood on her desk. David wilted near my feet, a gush of red staining his Gant shirt.

The firing continued, but I could not react. I was the omniscient third person at the adolescent massacre. I watched the killings and thought of Mary Hartman's kitchen floor while I tried to put my head in order.

I don't know when it stopped, because time and space had frozen. I remember wondering why I was alive, then how I would tell all the parents, and how would the brothers be apprehended.

My feet started to vibrate in strange shakes. I could not

stop them. My hands were still but my shoes were rocking. I looked down to will them into tranquillity and saw bloody Dave laughing his head off. Maria looked up and giggled.

One by one, the tattered corpses came to life from perfected death falls rehearsed for weeks. Mike and Milton blew on their guns like the bronco busters of the beer commercials and grinned ear to ear.

I still could not speak.

Valerie laughed like morning sunshine.

Sam belted out a "Yahoo" that brought Sonia and Bettina back to the living.

The drama coach came in and asked if something was wrong.

I couldn't answer.

He didn't notice anything, so he left.

A maintenance man popped in to ask if the lights were okay, since he'd heard a popping noise, he thought.

I just pointed above me and he saw they were functioning, which I clearly was not.

They laughed like thunder; one would set off the other.

"If you coulda seen your face!"

"Dave's fall was the best."

"We almost made a Pan Am sign, but it woulda wrecked the surprise."

I think my color came back, and I laughed out of sheer relief. The Johnston brothers stood tall and packed their six-shooters back into their pockets.

Arnold got it all on film. A slide show to music was presented two weeks later.

My colleagues were scandalized.

"They're sick, I tell you; there's no limits anymore."

"Kick them out."

"Next time it'll be real."

"Did you recommend them for testing?"

"Their father is sensible; he'll attend to this, since he's an engineer."

"And they're both so good at math."

Like Boo Radley, the Johnston boys had finally come out. In retrospect, it was a brilliant coup of psychodrama, although I wouldn't like many more.

Wordsworth called poetry "the spontaneous overflow of powerful feelings recollected in tranquillity." I would add to that, "then shared with those you pick."

One fellow teacher told me in a flush of "total honesty" that if I really looked at it, I'd see . . .

You get what you deserve.

Okay. I'll take it.

Notes from the Underground

Please have a hot time giving me a D or better cause I tried hard to come most of the time. Besides I need it for football
I like the way you dress funny

Dave S.

I didn't mean to say shine it bitch when I walked out.
I meant to say catch you on the late freight.

Tim

Since you know me as a man of few words, I won't spoil your ideal. For my final I have decided that *Lord Jim* was a good book.

Steve

I'm still waiting for feminism to flee your body so you'll break down and have a kid

Mazeltov

Sara

From the desk of

Larry Swanson, Director Special Ed.

TO: M. Martin

RE: For your information

Jane Sherman	Gifted
Paul Raider	Not Gifted
Lyle Timber	Not Gifted
Joyce Shiffman	Gifted
Peter Thaleson	Not Gifted
Rona Stein	Not Gifted*

*Overachiever

he grabbed his erected member
and began to pound it in a fury of self hate.
God.
he cursed that omniscient bastard
through clenched teeth
and half shut eyes.

he masturbated for his
dead mother he masturbated

because he never knew to
love her

She was sucked out of this world into eternal silence by some supreme being. he was 3. there would be no replacement

So now, sitting in the bathroom on the toilet seat, he makes his cock cry for her. he thinks of young girls, young compared to his mother.
it is all the same. He wants a female to touch him. not physically,
but lovingly.

E.

when it comes to self,
i am insecure

My mother died this morning.
I was with her at the hospital
and the nuns were very nice
about everything.
Religiously she was ready
even though she was only forty.
I don't know what I'm
going to do about the kids
yet.
I came to school because
I think she would want
me to go on.

J.

My dad is using again
he steals from us all the time,
My mom and I hide the money
we make because junkies steal
from anyone. He's sick I
know that but what can I do,
I love my father.

G.

I tried Bartleby's approach
to peaceful refusal.
My mom told me to clear
the table and I said
"I would prefer
not to" just like he did
all calm and polite
Well she threw mash potatoes
in my face so I'm switching
to Girls' Chorus where it's
safer.

Cindy

Christmas was a bummer
My grandparents came out
from New York and my
Grandpa died in my
dad's bedroom.
I watched them take

the body, but I didn't
cry.
   Everybody was depressed
after that.

Kittie

I think we're all missing something.
We read about minority groups and poverty-stricken
people who go out and break things and murder people.
True, but then why do the high-middle-class-white-La Jolla-type people have such a high suicide rate? Especially
amongst "happy young people with so much to live for."
   Why do they kill each other,
      and we kill ourselves?

Karen

TO: Melody
FROM: The Pink Floyd Contingency

Thought you and your Karma would enjoy the enclosed brochure on the Maharishi University. You might give some consideration to the meditative approach since yours makes noise. What do you have to lose?

Dear My Parents,

How are you. Are you nice everyday. November is more end. I'm stay here at five and half months. School I have this writting a letter now. I'm a hateful! Because I'm not understand English yet and everytime is perplexed as well. Japan is nice weather now, for study and sport.

A food is good in one year and every day is cool. A match here is very hot. I was the skin a little browned in biting sun. Soon I will black.

I'm not translate English into Japanese and everytime I have a stare to dictionary. However no good. I should must study harder English. I have to learn to fast. I wish write many a things. But I'm no write. Then the end a letter.

Good Bye,
From
Mutsuko*

Words Offstage

Taking the roof off the house on Sundays
would reveal a girl
alone
with three dogs
Those who know her best.
Beyond the pasture of sheep,
the majestic Eucalyptus tree,
the driveway lined with daisies
lies the beach
producing spectacular sunsets
sometimes showing a distant island

* Mutsuko was a Japanese girl from Tokyo who was placed in my class because I had an extra chair. She spoke no English but learned rather quickly. She worried about anxious letters from her parents, who scolded her for not writing. She wrote every day. The mystery was solved by a classmate who saw her mail a letter in the PUSH slot of a blue trash can, which bore an uncanny resemblance to a mailbox.

reminding her of ecstasy at distant beaches.
Classmates and acquaintances
monopolize the sand
Holding figure, tan, pot and sex contests
Being organic and natural
  It seems unrealistic and drives her away
  to her big
  dark
  and lonely
  house,
With her three dogs.
  School provides people
yet, makes her lonelier still.
  All the cute surfers
with the cheerleaders of their sect.
the surfer girls
made of granola, honey
  and plastic
  gather in their area
She tries them for a while
but tires of the game
She's been told she's theatrical
but she's not like the people
involved in drama;
they search for a fire inside
their souls she knows isn't there
they too climb the ladder
trodding upon her as they go.

The teacher, a master of the art
believes the people
condoning their behavior
He laughs at her for being honest
with herself
and those around
when she doesn't see the magic on stage
in which
everyone else
seems to be reveling.

she knows there is a good element
to everything
Christians have God
Diets have water
She has a teacher
She admires and adores
She knows she has empathy
  and cares
  about the girl
  from the state
  held on a platter of golden sunshine
  where
she dwells
  alone
    and
  depressed.

Magdelena

Ms. Martin,

I talked to my mom last night and she said you said I should be going to a school that makes me think. Well I just thought I'd set you straight, my views on the Bible and Christianity have been challenged more in the last two weeks than ever before.

Some of my profs believe in Christian humanism which says man is basically good with some bad tendencies. Another feels that the Old Testament accounts of Creation are probably myths to explain things. Anyway I thought I should tell you I was not living in an intellectual vacuum.

Some of the kids feel sex before marriage is ok, a few even drink and smoke pot so it's not just a goody two shoes place. The only thing is no dancing, a rip off. There are a lot of fine women, even some liberated ones (Biblically misguided)

I have found out that people here are just as superficial in their judgments as anywhere else. No Christians aren't perfect, just forgiven!

I wish my brother would reconsider about his Bar Mitzvah.

Agape,
Donald

Just wanted to tell you that as of the first of March I am officially changing my name. My dad chose Kathryn because it was his mother's name. Since he left us I've been thinking about how shitty he was to my mom and he never even sends a card to my little brother even if it's his birthday.

He hit my mom when he was mad just like Tom hit Myrtle in *Gatsby* except that Tom bought her clothes which is more than my dad did. I don't hate him even if he's a dick he's my dad but I'm not going to keep the name he gave me so please after Mar. 1 call me "Bird."

Thank you.

I asked my mom if I could have a guitar and she told me to ask my dad. Since I've been studying about women I tested her out and said

"Your my mother and half of the
authority, you give me an answer."
"I have a hard enough time getting
stuff for myself."
"But mom you're his wife, you
should get what you want."
"OK then you sleep with him and
see if it's worth it."

I don't know what to make of this.

Doreen

Martinski,

Women's Lib drives me up the wall. I'll believe it when a girl I take out for the second time buys.

When your poor you need womens lib but when it comes down to it only one out of 100 are believers.

If your husband ever doesn't want to go out, call me up.

You can buy.

555-1818 Ask for Tony

Melody Martin ✧ ✧ ✧

Put your $ where your mouth is.

You say I can't afford you
when I say I've got to have you
So I planned the date we'll
have when I'm 25 and you're 40 and
losing your looks.
    Fly to San Francisco
    Taxi to town
    Drink at the Hyatt Regency
    Dinner at Benihana
    After dinner drink Top of the Mark
    Disco, cruising, nightclub
    The best fuck of your
    life at the hotel of your
    choice.
Breakfast in bed (expresso + croissants)
A new outfit for you to cheer you up cuz
you're old
Limo to the airport
Lunch in L. A. at Rangoon Racquet Club
Back home where you'll
be crazy about me. Hot, huh?
                    Back packer
                        ** Yes

TO: M. Martin
FROM: Stan Rumland, Principal
RE: Urinating on class time

Please do not leave your room unattended for whatever reason. This is a violation of the California Ed. Code. Call me if you need to leave.

S. R.

TO: S. R.
FROM: M. M.
RE: I have to leave to call you.

M. M.

TO: M. M.
FROM: S. R.
RE: Send a student.

S. R.

Letter published in a local paper:

A few days ago I heard some parents on TV who were criticizing the media for types of programs being produced. It is fortunate that we may make choices, and we have the option of turning to other channels or turning it off. However, it seems rather futile to complain on the one hand about television, when on the other hand, our children are the innocent victims of atheist teachers who, with the approval of book committees, subsequently approved by the board of education, assign their classes books to read such as *Catcher in the Rye, One Flew Over the Cookoo's Nest, Metamorphosis, Double Helix, Teen Suicides—Too Young to Die, The Man Who Cried I Am, Equus, Bell Jar,* ad infinitum.

As a case in point, the *Catcher in the Rye* has 214 pages. In the first fifty pages, there are at least 86 instances of God's name used in vain, 30 damns, 11 SOBs, 19 bastards, and many others, including the well-known four letter words, so multiplying fifty by four, it gives you an idea of how many swearwords one can expect to see. The material is pornographic, the English abominable, the story has little point, and does anything but teach students what good English is. I would point out that these books have been given to the mentally gifted minor English classes, and upon inquiring of the school why such a book is allowed, we found that it is on the ninth grade reading list, and, yes, approved by the board of education.

I was appalled to learn this was on a ninth grade list, but the teacher was assigning it to 10th and 11th graders. The next book she recommended was *The Man Who Cried I Am.* Since I do not care to pollute my mind by reading the whole thing, may I suggest that you look at the book (it is authored by John A. Williams) and just for openers, read the first page and 157; it should tell you something.

I am sure if the taxpayers knew that their tax dollars in part go for trashy literature of this kind, they would be up in arms; unfortunately, not too many parents take enough interest to see what their children are reading. It is heartbreaking to realize that beautiful children with brilliant minds can be subjected in public schools to this kind of teaching. If it were used to point out what not to do, there might be some validity, but then how many terrible trashy books must be given to show the same thing?

The paper replies:

It is surprising that books such as *Catcher in the Rye* are touted as literature for children 14 and 15 to read. This is indicative of just how far we have departed from the original intent for public schools laid down by the founding fathers of our country.

Many people think the U.S. Supreme Court has set the stage for this condition by rulings which have struck down mandatory prayer in schools, etc. My understanding of the high court's ruling is that it stresses secularism (i.e. the belief that religion should not enter into public education) to a point, but the main emphasis is one of balance. It is O.K. to teach about the Bible in school as well as to have prayer, but one must not try to proselytize (i.e. try to make converts to a particular religion).

Many teachers seem to think that all they can do is teach evolution, relativistic ethics, and modern (in many cases pornographic) literature. But these involve a faith position in that one has to take a metaphysical (beyond physical or material) position to explain his starting points. Here is where the idea of balance comes into play and the people who believe in God have every right to present the other side. This sense of balance is sorely missing in today's schools.

Children need to know about God so that they can decide for themselves what to believe. Presenting only the dark side of life is a tremendous mistake for our local school boards and its affect is seen throughout the country. Keep battling, your cause is worth the effort. Our children hold the country's future. They need to become prepared for tomorrow's leadership."

* * *

TO: M. Martin
FROM: Stan Rumland, Principal
RE: There are some people here who sure don't like you. What are these books? I hope you're following procedure. Also, according to my watch, you were 40 seconds late to class. Please be in your room as soon as the bell has rang.

S. R.

I touch
  but do not feel.
I cry, but tears
  do not fall.
I must be strong,
  uncaring
Men have no time for love.
I am told I must fight
I must die for causes
I don't know or understand
They tell me it is an honor
  to die thus
I'm frightened and do not want to die
Be a man they say!
Don't think of right or wrong

Do what is expected of you
    For the cause
    Be strong
And yet I feel so helpless
    The spider web around
    us suffocates
    in dialogue
        of the posthumous medal

Duke

We the undersigned think you should at least tell us why you're so crabby today. You yelled at Steve when he didn't do anything. You didn't answer Eric's question, and besides nobody's read that stupid book because who *cares* about a guy obsessed with a whale?

At least check one of the following if you won't talk:

___ I had a fight with my husband
___ We don't have any money
___ I hate kids cuz they're young and I'm not
___ I'm in that time of the month
___ No fault depression
___ Sick
___ Life is meaningless

English 9
Period 5

Melody Martin ✧ ✧ ✧

Memorable Quotes of Pedagogical Wisdom

From a "How to Study" lecture in Teacher's Ed.:

"Students may not be encouraged to study in the home. There are many reasons for this. Parents may be uneducated, therefore cannot appreciate the value of education. Or they may be moronic, psychotic, or have abnormal values."

On the use of drama in English for low achievers:

"The first creative experience for the incompetent child must be carefully guided, for like the mating of the boar, if first attempt is unsuccessful, it may never take to the sow again."

From a reading expert about labs and special children:

"We don't try to make a silk purse out of a sow's ear. We find a sow's head to stick it on."

Visiting professor from Australia's comment on educationally handicapped children:

"These children are the sand in the educational machinery."

Voices chatter like
   the nagging wife
Oh the noise!
Peace will come one day

And memories of
your room
shall remain in the
clatter of my memory.
Anne

This class is stupid
You are stupid
You know nothing
about my feelings
So jolly well butt out!
All my love,
Anthony

For your sake, your sanity
and your safety do not
remain in this line of
business
Victor

Sweet Somethings

Damn that Admiral Rickover and the silver satellite!

We were the children of Sputnik whose futures were planned with a hefty shove toward math and science, and a warning that the Communist could wipe us out unless we took those trig and physics classes with feverish dedication.

The space age.

That magical term that forced us all to slog through molecular structures, secrets of fusion, and chromosomes in synapse with an enthusiasm and knowledge that America was waiting for us.

And we believed them.

Oh, how we trusted that the future belonged to those with the sheepskin deliciously engraved with a higher degree.

The senior counselor who looked like a mosquito in a hair net went so far as to tell us an astounding statistic.

The average college graduate earns approximately one

hundred thousand dollars more than the non-college graduate.

I'm still waiting for my check.

But then I never really understood higher math, where dots on the blackboard suddenly become teacups.

I was more fond of the obtuse in the world than in an angle.

My classmates seemed to love it. They went on to Cal Tech, Stanford, MIT, and Brandeis, armed with slide rules, deductive reasoning, and a solid background in the relationship of the axis to the fulcrum.

I went to France.

Ten years later we were reunited over turkey à la king, tired blue and white crepe paper, and a nervous paranoia about disappointing each other with what we'd become.

We did inherit the miracle of technology. And Vietnam. And drugs. And broken dreams of unemployment.

There were success stories.

One girl is a Washington lawyer, her high school goals reached with ease.

A couple of guys made a killing in surfboards.

The top science student dropped out of Cal Tech and into acid tablets, found God, lost a marriage, and is presently editing a jogging magazine in Northern California.

The girl most likely to succeed went to New York and had a child by a famous artist whom she named after a Foster Kleiser billboard that caught her fancy.

A mousy girl with glasses and oily hair is now living in a free love commune in the south of France and is "looking for a daddy to hug me."

The campus beatnik sells mutual funds in Des Moines.

Twenty-seven guys died in the war.

The most promising artist, who was also a basketball star, is throwing two-hundred-dollar pots in a beach town and skulking about, masquerading as an ascetic ass bandit.

One half of the class is on a second marriage. Thirteen people have doctorates in science; five have jobs they deserve.

The cherub voted "Most Freckles," which meant nobody would sleep with her, is a psychologist who counsels women.

The boy with the deformed foot went on to play for the Rams, the Saints, and the Eagles.

Most claim they are happy.

I choose to believe that.

I think about my students all the time. Letters come with joyful regularity.

A favorite curly-haired delight is studying the Supreme Court and The Constitution with Archibald Cox.

Another has his own nursery school and is expecting his first child in March.

Some are in the foreign service.

Most are still confused over what will happen next.

Love has come and gone and, to most, come again.

Some have money.

Others have opted for personal satisfaction and have given up possessions.

I wonder about the ones who don't keep in touch.

I'll tell you a secret. A dream if you will, but I rerun it so often at my fantasy film festival that it's real to me.

I want to have a party, a big one, five years from now. Every kid who's ever crossed my path will be there. I'll meet their spouses, hug their kids, and remember them when they had flat stomachs, full heads of hair, and no wrinkles.

I plan to be smashing. I'll diet for months before, over-henna my hair, and hope they don't notice that age has not dealt kindly with me.

I'll listen to their tales, and if they don't make sense, I'll make up my own meaning.

The food will be sumptuous and elegant, paid for by those who have struck it rich. They will provide the music, since several are marvelously talented. We won't lie to each other about our lives.

I plan to take the mike and tell them one thing.

Last year I *saw* Sputnik at the Russian Exhibition in Los Angeles, and it was only a shiny silver ball in which I saw the reflection of my face.

They will remember me fondly; after all, it's my dream.

In the middle of the evening, I'll be the only one who's tired, and my mascara will be running into my crow's-feet. I'll sneak off to the ladies' room, where the medical students can't guess my fatigue, and rest for a bit with a glass of sherry.

Then I'm going to find a secret place, preferably a dimly lit cloakroom, and just watch them.

All of them.

I intend to become shamefully sentimental.

Melody Martin ✧ ✧ ✧

When I was a young girl, I read *The Catcher in the Rye* under the covers with a flashlight. I will never forget the scene near the end where Holden goes to say good-bye to his sister Phoebe before he runs away from home. She insists that she will go too.

He takes her to the park and buys her a ticket for the carrousel. She gives him back his red hunting cap and he sits on a bench and watches her go round and round. It is a moment of joy, for him, for her, for me.

He said "she looked so damn *nice*," whizzing by again and again, that he was "damn near bawling."

And I cried too.

I was there, Holden.

I still am, in my heart.